COLLINS GEM

VEGETARIAN FOOD

Jane Bowler
Consultant: Fiona Hunter

HarperCollins*Publishers*

HarperCollins Publishers
P. O. Box, Glasgow G4 0NB

First published 1993

Reprint 10 9 8 7 6 5 4 3 2 1 0

© Book Creation Services Ltd 1993

ISBN 0 00 470117 8

Printed in Great Britain by
HarperCollins Manufacturing, Glasgow

Introduction

The Gem Guide to Vegetarian Food is an easy-to-use pocket reference book. It offers an accessible introduction to the wide variety of foods available to those who either already follow a vegetarian diet or are considering doing so.

There are entries for fruits, vegetables, pulses, nuts, seeds, grains, soya products, dairy products and store-cupboard items, which provide information on choosing and storing foods for freshness, nutritional value and how to prepare each food. Appetizing suggestions for uses are also given.

The introduction explains why vegetarianism has become more popular in recent years, and gives advice on moving to a vegetarian diet and maintaining healthy nutrition.

Where foods are known by more than one name these are given, and useful and appropriate cross-references are given in **bold** lettering.

What is a Vegetarian?

Increasingly, more people are turning to an exclusively or a predominantly vegetarian diet. In the UK there are an estimated 3.6 million vegetarians and millions more who have stopped eating red meat, sometimes described as 'demi-vegetarians'. Many people, however, are still uncertain of exactly what 'vegetarian' means.

Simply, vegetarians do not eat any food that involves the killing of animals. Therefore, all meat, poultry, game, fish and shellfish are excluded from their diet. Dairy products and eggs are suitable for vegetarians. However, since vegetarianism was first advocated, advances in the food and farming industries have seen the advent of a number of other foods which are not considered suitable for vegetarians.

Many people who choose a vegetarian diet for ethical reasons are disturbed by certain methods of animal husbandry involved in intensive farming, and having ceased to eat meat, take their ethical stance further by refusing to buy or eat eggs produced in intensive 'battery' farming systems. For strict vegetarians, any foods made with battery eggs, including quiches, cakes and even 'vegetarian' burgers, are considered unsuitable.

The modern diet includes a variety of convenience foods, manufactured outside the home. In order for such foods to have a long shelf life and an attractive appearance, or to improve their taste and texture, most convenience foods contain food additives. Some of the chemicals and compounds used as food additives are derived from slaughtered animals. Examples include gelatine (made from waste connective tissues), animal rennet (derived from the stomach lining of young calves) and certain 'E' numbers, such as E120 (cochineal), a red colouring made from beetles. Even though such additives are used in foods in tiny quantities, people who are vegetarian for ethical reasons do their best to avoid consuming them. This requires a good deal of knowledge about food production and the careful scrutiny of food labels, and has led to the introduction of products such as 'vegetarian cheese' made without animal rennet.

Vegans are people who eat no animal produce at all, either for ethical reasons or because they do not believe that a diet containing animal products is good for the health. This means that their diet is basically vegetarian, but they go further by not eating eggs, milk, cheese or any dairy products, and many vegans even go so far as not eating honey. Many vegans also avoid wearing any animal products (including leather, silk and wool), or using any products, such as cosmetics or household cleaning products, which contain ingredients derived from animals.

A few people go further and become fruitarians, which means that they eat only fruit, nuts and seeds. Fruitarians believe that it is wrong to kill a plant by digging up its roots or stripping away its leaves for food. This, however, is not a balanced diet and is not recommended.

Two dietary systems often used in combination with vegetarianism are the Hay diet and the macrobiotic diet.

Hay diet

The Hay diet was devised by an American doctor, William Howard Hay, in the 1930s, and is known as 'food combining'. The principle of the diet is that certain foods, namely starches and proteins, react together when eaten at the same meal to render the meal indigestible. Therefore, foods are classed as protein or starch and not eaten at the same meal. The Hay diet is not necessarily vegetarian, but advocates eating mainly fresh fruit and vegetables, with some starches and protein, and some fats and sugars, although refined starches and sugars are to be avoided. Food combining has recently enjoyed a resurgence in popularity and is a regime that can be combined with a vegetarian diet.

Macrobiotic diet

The macrobiotic system of diet was devised in Japan in 1911, by George Ohsawa. This diet draws upon the ancient principles of Chinese medicine. Foods are classified as Yin (relaxing and cooling) or Yang (strengthening and warming), and intake is varied according to mood and personality with the aim of achieving a harmonious balance. The macrobiotic diet does not include meat, poultry, eggs or dairy products, and although fish and shellfish are permitted in moderation, these are not essential and many people who eat according to macrobiotic principles are either vegetarian or vegan. Some people who follow extreme macrobiotic diets consider the highest peak of achievement to be a diet consisting purely of boiled brown rice. This is not considered a healthy diet and is not recommended.

Many people who eat a vegetarian diet prefer to eat a wholefood diet wherever possible. A wholefood diet is one in which foods are eaten in an unrefined state. For example, fresh whole fruits and vegetables are purchased rather than canned fruits and vegetables, whole brown rice is preferred to milled white rice, wholemeal bread and pasta are preferred to bread and pasta made with white flour. A variety of unrefined grains, pulses and seeds are included in the diet, and refined, fatty and sugary artificial foods are avoided. Unrefined foods are likely to have a far superior nutritional content to refined foods, and are more likely to be lower in fat and sugar, and higher in dietary fibre and trace elements.

Many vegetarians are concerned over the levels of residues of chemical fertilizers, pesticides and fungicides found in fruit, vegetables, grains and pulses, and dairy produce. In response to this greater awareness, it is now possible to buy a larger range of organic food products, including flours and grains, bread, milk, cheese and yoghurt, and organically-grown fruit and vegetables from supermarkets and health-food shops. However, these tend to be more expensive than intensively produced foods, and are often available on a seasonal or local basis only.

The Health Dimension

A balanced lacto-vegetarian diet (a vegetarian diet that includes dairy products) can supply every essential vitamin and mineral required by the human body for good health. Such a diet can comply closely with government guidelines on healthy eating.

The vegetarian diet is generally higher in complex carbohydrates and lower in fat than the average UK diet. It is far lower in saturated fats than the average meat-based diet, as saturated fats are found mainly in animal foods. The vegetarian diet tends to be high in dietary fibre, and there is no dietary fibre in animal foods. It certainly does not lack protein and the government has recommended that protein should be obtained from plants as well as from animals. People who are vegetarian for health reasons are often very conscious of the importance of a balanced diet, and tend to chose wholefoods and additive-free foods, and to consume less salt and sugar. However, it must be stressed that these points apply only to a properly balanced vegetarian diet, and that vegetarians who live on convenience foods, chips and chocolate will not be improving their health through their diet.

Coronary heart disease is the largest single cause of death in the UK today. People who eat high levels of saturated fats, found almost entirely in meat and dairy products, may be subject to an increase in blood cholesterol levels and to a build-up of fatty deposits in the arteries around the heart. On average, vegetarians have a 20% lower blood cholesterol level than meat-eaters, and for this reason their chances of developing coronary heart disease are greatly reduced. Vegetarian diets have been shown to be capable of reducing blood pressure in patients with hypertension. Diets that are high in animal fats have also been linked with an increased incidence of breast cancer, ovarian cancer and cervical cancer.

Diets that are low in dietary fibre have been associated with a high incidence of colon cancer. A lack of dietary fibre in the diet slows the excretion of waste products from the digestive tract. Vegetarian diets have a much higher dietary fibre content than the average UK diet. This fibre intake also helps protect against constipation, haemorrhoids, varicose veins and diverticular disease.

Some people decide to stop eating meat because they are worried about the possible effects of chemical residues in meat, or because of fears of food poisoning or BSE (bovine spongiform encephalopathy). Many people who are concerned about their health find that opting for a vegetarian diet is a beneficial way of improving, and having greater control over, their health.

Vegetarian Nutrition

Many people enjoy experimenting with unusual vegetarian foods and, therefore, follow a nutritious and varied wholefood diet. There is a danger, however, that some people who have become vegetarian because of ethical reasons fail to adapt and develop their diets adequately to compensate for the loss of this major nutrient source, and a diet that consists solely of refined foods and sweet and fatty snacks cannot be considered a healthy one. There is an enormous variety of foods available to the vegetarian and it is important to try to maintain a balanced diet by eating as wide a range of foods as possible.

A vegetarian diet that includes fresh fruit and vegetables, cereals, nuts and pulses, soya products, yeast extract, free-range eggs and dairy products, should not be lacking in any essential nutrients.

Protein

Proteins are chains of amino acids. There are 20 amino acids in total and most can be manufactured in the body, but a few (eight in all) have to be supplied by the diet. Meat and animal foods contain all eight of these amino acids. Vegetable proteins, such as nuts, pulses and grains, do not contain all eight, but by including a wide variety of protein foods in the diet vegetarians can easily obtain all of them. Animal protein is sometimes called 'first-class protein', and plant protein is called 'second-class protein'.

In the past, it was argued that animal protein provided the perfect protein source, because the amino acids it contained were supplied in the correct proportions for the body to use. This led to the theory of protein combining, in which vegetarians were advised to eat two different sources of protein at every meal. For example, grains and pulses could be eaten together, or nuts and grains. By this method each meal would supply all eight amino acids for the body to use. However, it is now thought less important to combine proteins at each meal, because the body is thought to be able to store amino acids until the next meal provides suitable partners for them to be made into the chains that form proteins. Vegetarians should ensure that their diet contains a variety of different sources of protein. Although cheese and eggs supply good-quality protein they should not be relied upon as a meat replacement because they are high in saturated fats.

Fats

A high intake of saturated fats is associated with an increased risk of heart disease. Saturated fats are found predominantly in animal foods, and most vegetable oils (with the exception of coconut oil and palm oil) are high in polyunsaturated fats. In general, a vegetarian diet is likely to be much lower in saturated fats than a non-vegetarian diet.

Carbohydrate

Carbohydrate is the main source of energy in the
diet, and can take the form of sugars, starches or
complex carbohydrates (starch combined with
dietary fibre). There is no carbohydrate in meat,
eggs or dairy foods, apart from some milk sugar
(lactose) in milk. The main source of carbohydrate in the diet is plant foods, and it is advisable
to obtain most of the carbohydrate from starches
rather than sugars. Foods like wholemeal bread,
brown rice, cereals, root vegetables and pulses are
good sources of complex carbohydrate, which is
considered a particularly healthy source of energy. People who are vegetarian for health reasons
often follow a diet low in refined foods and sugars.

Dietary fibre

There is no dietary fibre in animal foods, so in
general a properly balanced vegetarian diet
should contain significantly more dietary fibre.
Many people who are vegetarian for health
reasons follow a diet rich in wholefoods, which is
also high in fibre.

Vitamins

Vitamin A as retinol is only found in animal foods,
including dairy products and egg yolk. However,
the body can manufacture vitamin A if its precursor carotene is supplied by the diet. Carotene is
available in abundance in red and yellow veg-

etables and fruits, such as carrots, tomatoes, apricots, pumpkins, and it is also found in green leafy vegetables.

All of the B vitamins except vitamin B_{12} are found in wholegrain cereals and in yeasts. Vitamin B_1 is also found in potatoes and lentils, vitamins B_2 and B_3 are found in dairy products, vitamins B_2 and B_6 are found in green leafy vegetables.

Vitamin B_{12} is not found in any plant foods, although traces of it are said to have been found in mushrooms, seaweeds, algae and fermented soya products. It is found in yeast extracts, and certain fortified foods, such as soya milk and breakfast cereals. Although vegans are advised to ensure a regular vitamin B_{12} intake by taking a supplement or using fortified foods, vegetarians who eat dairy products and eggs will obtain an adequate intake from these foods.

Folic acid and biotin are associated with the B complex vitamins. Folic acid is found in green leafy vegetables, wholegrains, nuts, brewer's yeast and milk. Biotin is found in yeast, mushrooms, milk and eggs.

Vitamin C is available in abundance from fresh fruit and vegetables, especially citrus fruits and green peppers. Vegetarians are unlikely to suffer from a deficiency of vitamin C, and an intake in excess of requirements is not harmful.

Vitamin D is another vitamin not found in plant foods. The body can manufacture vitamin D when the skin is exposed to sunlight, and can store the vitamin for use throughout the winter months. Vitamin D is also available from milk and dairy products. Some vegan foods are fortified with vitamin D. Vitamin D_3 is likely to have come from an animal source, but vitamin D_2 is always suitable for vegetarians.

Vitamin E is found in vegetable oils and margarines, and wholegrain cereals. Because of the oils used in cooking and in the manufacture of foods, vegetarians are unlikely to go short of vitamin E.

Minerals

Calcium is abundantly available in dairy products, leafy green vegetables, nuts and seeds and bread. Some soya milks are also fortified with calcium.

Magnesium and *phosphorus* work with calcium in the body and both are available in a wide variety of plant foods.

Iron is perhaps the mineral most likely to be deficient because meat is such an excellent source of well-absorbed iron. Indeed, vegetarians are often thought of as pale and anaemic. A balanced vegetarian diet, containing nuts, pulses, seeds and grains, leafy green vegetables, dried fruits, soya products and yeasts, should offer ample iron from a wide variety of sources. The absorption of iron is aided by consuming vitamin C at the same time, but hindered by drinking tea with the meal. Leafy green vegetables contain both iron and vitamin C.

Potassium is widely available in all fresh fruits and vegetables, nuts, soya beans and wholegrains.

Trace elements, such as chromium, copper, cobalt, fluoride, iodine, manganese, molybdenum, selenium and zinc, are more likely to be available from a diet that contains a good amount of unrefined wholefoods than from a diet of highly-refined foods. All of the trace elements are available in a wide range of plant foods. The amount of iodine in vegetables also depends upon soil quality. Dairy products and seaweeds are good sources of iodine. Zinc availability is often affected by the presence of phytic acid in foods, but the zinc in breads made with yeast is available for absorption.

Lacto-vegetarians (vegetarians who eat dairy products) should not need to supplement their diets to obtain any vitamins or minerals. Vegans may need to consider taking vitamin B_{12} supplements. It is especially important to maintain an adequate intake of vitamin B_{12} during pregnancy and also during breast-feeding. It is very common for women to be prescribed iron tablets during pregnancy, regardless of their diets. The government does not specify a recommended daily intake for vitamin D as it is thought that requirements can easily be satisfied by the action of sunlight on the skin. However, people who do not eat dairy products, who are confined indoors or have religious beliefs that involve covering most of the skin, may need to consider taking a vitamin D supplement. If vegetarians do feel that their nutritional intake is compromised for a variety of reasons, such as they cannot afford to buy a wide range of foods, or they do not have the time or space to prepare fresh foods, or because they have no appetite after illness, or they feel that their environment is so polluted that it causes a great drain on their body's nutritional resources, it is best to take a balanced, multivitamin supplement rather than to focus on supplementing any particular vitamin or mineral. Over-supplementation of one vitamin or mineral can affect the absorption of another micronutrient. It is now thought that in many cases the human body can adapt to a diet without meat by increasing its ability to absorb vitamins and minerals from plant sources.

A well-balanced lacto-vegetarian diet should include a regular intake (not necessarily daily) from the following groups: pulses, nuts and seeds; wholegrain cereals; fresh fruit; dried fruit; fresh vegetables and salads; soya products; vegetable oils; yeast extract.

Modern vegetarian recipe books take nutritional requirements into account and often offer nutritional assessment of recipes and menu planning suggestions.

Special Needs

Pregnancy

It is perfectly possible to remain vegetarian throughout pregnancy and breast-feeding (see below). Some pregnant vegetarian women feel that theirs is a wise choice, because they are worried about food poisoning and other hazards associated with the preparation and storage of meat. All pregnant women and new mothers are advised to pay special attention to their diets and the same is true for vegetarians. During pregnancy, a well-balanced vegetarian diet can be supplemented with special foods chosen for their nutritional value, including wheat germ, brewer's yeast, soya flour, molasses and yeast extract.

According to the latest government figures, the only increases in recommended daily intake of nutrients during pregnancy are as follows:

vitamin A – extra 100 microgram daily
thiamin – extra 0.1 milligram daily in the third trimester only
riboflavin – extra 0.3 mg daily
folic acid – extra 100 µg daily
vitamin C – extra 10 mg daily
vitamin D – extra 10 µg daily

Introduction

The recommended Calorific intake for women aged between 19 and 50 is 1,940 Calories. In the third trimester of pregnancy this should be increased by an extra 200 Calories per day. This is not a great increase, and may be due to the fact that during the third trimester when a woman is heavily pregnant her level of activity may not be as high as usual.

Protein

Protein requirements are increased during pregnancy from 45 grams (g) per day for women aged between 19 and 50 to 51 g per day. In pregnancy, protein foods are used to help build the baby's body and when planning a diet for pregnancy it is useful to focus on a core of protein foods. Good sources of protein for vegetarians include dairy products and eggs, soya products, pulses, nuts and grains. It is important to remember to eat a variety of different protein foods, so that all eight essential amino acids are represented in the diet.

Since protein foods are used primarily for growth during pregnancy, it is important to provide a good carbohydrate intake for energy requirements. Complex carbohydrates that offer both starch and dietary fibre are ideal in pregnancy as they offer both energy and dietary fibre to help avoid constipation and haemorrhoids, both of which are common in pregnancy. Complex carbohydrates include potatoes, bread, pasta, rice and bananas.

A diet that is very high in dietary fibre, however, may have an adverse effect, in that a mother may feel full, but may not have obtained the full complement of vitamins, minerals and energy-rich foods that her body requires. For this reason, it is advisable to combine an intake of complex carbohydrates with a good intake of fats, such as nuts and nut spreads, vegetable oils and margarine, because these help to boost energy levels.

Vitamins

The requirements for vitamin A increase by 100 µg during pregnancy, from 600 to 700 µg daily. Vegetarians obtain vitamin A as retinol from dairy products and eggs, and as beta-carotene from a wide variety of plant foods.

Good vegetarian sources of vitamin B are brewer's yeast, yeast extract, dairy products, eggs, soya products, wheatgerm, wholegrains, nuts, pulses and seeds. There is no extra requirement of vitamin B_3, B_6 or B_{12} in pregnancy. The requirement for vitamin B_2 rises from 1.1 mg per day to 1.4 mg per day. There is no additional requirement of vitamin B_6.

Vitamin B_{12} is important because it is absent from plant foods, and a deficiency can lead to nerve damage in the baby. However, a good intake of vitamin B_{12} should allow the baby to be born with a pool of the vitamin already stored in his or her body. The suggested intake of vitamin B_{12} is 1.5 µg daily, and this can be achieved easily by including dairy products or fortified foods in the diet, or by taking a vitamin B_{12} supplement.

Folic acid is extremely important during pregnancy, because it is involved with the manufacture of DNA and RNA, the chains of genetic information that we have in every cell in our bodies. It also helps prevent anaemia. Deficiency has recently been implicated in the incidence of spina bifida. For this reason some doctors believe that all pregnant women, regardless of dietary preference, should be routinely given folic acid supplements. The suggested intake of folic acid is 300 µg daily, and vegetarian foods that contain folic acid include leafy green vegetables, brewer's yeast, yeast extract, root vegetables, whole and sprouted grains, black-eyed beans, milk, eggs, dates, mushrooms, orange juice and peanuts. Folic acid is very unstable and a high proportion is destroyed in cooking. It is helpful, therefore, to include raw vegetables in the diet, perhaps by eating a salad every day. Also, quickly stir-frying foods can produce a hot meal with minimal nutrient loss.

Vitamin C is widely available in a balanced vegetarian diet. It is found in citrus fruits and fruit juices, and in many other fruits and vegetables including peppers, spinach and broccoli. Because the body cannot store vitamin C it is important to have a daily intake of around 50 mg.

Vitamin D works with calcium to help form the baby's bones, teeth and muscles. Generally, the body can manufacture all the vitamin D it requires during the summer months, when the skin is exposed to sunlight, and vitamin D can be stored in the body to cover winter requirements. However, if a pregnant mother feels that she is not getting enough sunshine, and is not eating many dairy foods, she should consider supplementing her diet with an intake of around 10 µg of vitamin D daily, which should be continued while she is breast-feeding.

Intake of vitamin E is very rarely a problem as the minimum intake is 3 mg daily, but in practice daily intake is usually far higher than this. Vitamin E is supplied in the vegetarian diet by nuts, oils and wholegrains.

Minerals and Trace Elements

The human body's ability to absorb calcium from foods varies according to the amount of calcium available in the diet. If the diet is low in calcium, the body will extract a lot of the calcium available, whereas if calcium is abundant in the diet, the body will take only what it requires. It is thought that a daily diet containing 700–800 mg is sufficient. There is no increased requirement for calcium during pregnancy because the body naturally becomes more efficient at extracting calcium from foods at this time. However, calcium intake can be compromised if the diet is low in vitamin D, as vitamin D is necessary for the absorption of calcium. A baby is unlikely to be damaged if a pregnant mother's diet is low in calcium, because the body is able to compensate by taking calcium for the baby from the mother's own teeth and bones. It is important, therefore, to ensure that the diet contains ample calcium to avoid bone and dental depletion. Vegetarians obtain calcium from dairy products, soya products (including fortified soya milk), pulses, nuts, leafy green vegetables and dried fruit.

Anaemia is often a problem in pregnancy and many doctors prescribe iron tablets almost as a matter of routine, regardless of diet. A pregnant woman should be able to satisfy her requirements for iron by maintaining an intake similar to that before she became pregnant. The UK government has suggested that there need be no increase in the recommended daily consumption of 15 mg during pregnancy. This is because while they are not pregnant women loose blood and iron monthly during their menstrual period. Periods stop during pregnancy so this loss of iron ceases. Vegetarian sources of iron include leafy green vegetables, wholegrains, lentils and dried fruits. It is important to note that vegetarian sources of iron are less easily absorbed by the body than animal sources, and although the body becomes extra efficient at obtaining the iron it needs from the foods supplied during pregnancy, vegetarians would be wise to aim for a high iron intake. Vegetarian foods that can be used as iron supplements during pregnancy include wheat germ, molasses and brewer's yeast. Some vegetarian nutritionists recommend that a tablespoon of each should be included in the daily diet at this time. Molasses can be dissolved in a drink and it is also rich in calcium. Wheat germ and brewer's yeast can be sprinkled over meals during the day and also offer useful B complex vitamins. Including a good source of vitamin C, such as a piece of fruit, at each meal helps the body to absorb iron, whereas drinking tea, which contains tannin, during a meal can hinder the body's ability to absorb iron.

Zinc intake is important during pregnancy as diets low in zinc have been associated with a greater incidence of miscarriage and birth defects. Zinc helps the body to absorb B vitamins and to use protein for growth. Vegetarian foods that contain zinc include wheat germ and wheat bran, wholegrains, seeds, nuts, pulses and dairy foods along with most of the foods for vegetarians which are rich in iron. Although the UK government does not specify an increased zinc requirement during pregnancy, because the body becomes more efficient at absorbing zinc during pregnancy, it is important for vegetarians to be aware that in many cases the zinc in vegetarian foods is mostly unavailable. This is due to the binding action of phytic acid in high-fibre foods. The recommended intake for zinc is 7 mg per day. Cooking frees zinc from phytic acid and does not destroy it, and it is thought that wholemeal bread is an especially good source of zinc for vegetarians.

Introduction

A properly balanced vegetarian diet, which contains a good proportion of unrefined foods, should not be deficient in any trace elements, and there is no increased requirement for any of the trace elements during pregnancy. The requirement of magnesium is 270 mg daily, and this can be supplied by nuts, grains and pulses. The requirements for phosphorus is 50 mg for those over 19 and 625 mg for those under, and this can be provided from eggs, dairy products, nuts and grains. The requirement for iodine, which is found in dairy products, is 140 µg daily. It is found in some vegetables, but the content depends upon the amount of iodine in the soil where the vegetables were grown. The best source of iodine for vegetarians is seaweed. Tablets of kelp are available and can be used as a supplement, or powdered kelp can be sprinkled onto meals once or twice weekly.

Dietary Fibre

A vegetarian diet is naturally high in dietary fibre, and there is no dietary fibre in meat or animal foods. A good fibre intake can help prevent haemorrhoids and constipation, which are common in pregnancy. It is not necessary, however, to use a dietary fibre supplement, such as bran, during a vegetarian pregnancy because this can increase the amount of phytic acid in the diet. Such an increase would inhibit the body's ability to absorb certain minerals.

Breast-feeding

The recommended diet during breast-feeding is slightly different to that recommended during pregnancy. An increased intake of all nutrients is advised and it is recommended that this should be achieved by simply eating more; increasing the Calorific intake by the following: 0-1 month plus 450 kcal per day; 1-2 months plus 530 kcal per day; 2-3 months plus 570 kcal per day. The intake of protein should be increased by the following amounts: 0-6 months plus 11 g per day; 6 months and after plus 8 g per day. The intake of calcium should be around 1200 mg daily.

The amount of vitamin C, thiamin, riboflavin and, to a lesser extent, pantothenic acid, pyridoxine, biotin, folic acid and vitamin B_{12} in the diet is reflected in the nutritional quality of the breast milk produced, and it is important to ensure that the diet offers good amounts of these nutrients as breast milk is the only food given to a baby for several months. The amount of other nutrients in the diet is not reflected in the breast milk. Although if calcium is deficient in the diet, the mother's body withdraws calcium from her own bones and teeth to make the breast milk. Consequently, though the quality of the breast milk should not be compromised, the bodily health of a breast-feeding mother, whose diet does not supply all necessary nutrients, could be jeopardized. Vegan nursing mothers should be particularly careful to ensure that their intake of vitamin D is adequate, and they are advised to also take vitamin B_{12} supplements because breast milk deficient in vitamin B_{12} could cause nerve damage to a baby who is fed only on breast milk for several months.

Babies and Young Children

A diet consisting almost entirely of breast milk or infant formula satisfies all the nutritional requirements of a baby up to the age of three to four months. Thereafter, breast or bottle milk must remain a major part of the diet, but solids can be gradually introduced.

Babies have a very small capacity for food and cannot eat much. The vegetarian diet tends often to be a diet rich in wholefoods and bulky fibrous foods. Such foods are not suitable for babies, because they offer bulk without an equal amount of nutritional value. It would be dangerous for a baby to satisfy his or her appetite without having been able to obtain all the minerals and vitamins he or she requires.

Protein

Babies need a high intake of protein because they are growing very rapidly. From birth to six months the recommended protein intake is one gram for every pound of body weight, each day. This intake gradually goes down proportionately, so that at the age of one to three years a child requires around 14.5 g daily, regardless of body weight.

Babies, as with adults, require a variety of plant protein foods in order to obtain all the essential amino acids for protein building. There are eight essential amino acids for adults, but nine for growing children because they are unable to manufacture histidine in their bodies.

Good protein foods for babies and children include wheat germ, tahini, puréed, cooked pulses and grains, ground nuts and mashed tofu. Later, and with care, cooked egg yolks and dairy products, such as natural yoghurt made with whole milk, cottage cheese and finely-grated hard cheese, can be introduced.

Minerals

Babies and children need a high intake of calcium for building strong bones. The daily requirement up to the age of one year is 525 mg, but at the age of one to three years it falls to around 350 mg. Breast and bottle milk are excellent sources of calcium, but it is not wise to introduce dairy products, such as cows' milk into the diet at too early an age. Good alternative calcium sources are dark green vegetables, tofu, ground nuts and carob flour.

Babies also need a relatively high iron intake because they are growing rapidly. Between birth and three months the daily intake should be around 1.7 mg daily, rising to 4.3 mg between four and six months and 7.8 mg daily between seven and twelve months, and then reducing slightly to 6.9 mg daily from one to five years of age. Suitable iron sources for babies and young children include prune juice, tofu and soya milk, soaked and puréed dried fruits, cooked and puréed pulses and cereals, and fresh fruit and vegetables, especially as finger foods. It is also helpful to get into the habit of offering a food or drink rich in vitamin C with every meal, because this helps the body to absorb iron.

Vitamins

Vitamins A, C and D can be obtained from similar foods to those recommended for adults, but ensure that they are suitably prepared. These vitamins are also available in the form of vitamin drops and the UK government recommends that all babies between the ages of six months and two (or, in some cases, five) years should be given these to ensure that their nutritional requirements are met. The B complex vitamins can be supplied by cooked and puréed grains, some vegetables, yeast extract and (when the child is old enough) dairy products. It is particularly important for vegetarian and vegan children to be given vitamin B_{12} sources so that they are able to build up a store of the vitamin in their bodies for possible later use. Children can be given yeast extract, fortified soya milks (not in place of breast or bottle milk), or a crushed vitamin B_{12} tablet. Some vitamin drops for children contain vitamin B_{12} as well as vitamins A, C and D.

When planning the diet of a vegetarian baby or child, it is crucial to remember to provide foods which supply the requirements of protein, iron, calcium and vitamin B_{12}. Many doctors do not recommend a vegan diet for babies or children, and such children must be given a vitamin B_{12} supplement and possibly also supplements of calcium and iron.

Older People

In later life, good nutrition can help protect the immune system, warding off common diseases which can have a more serious affect on older people. Research has shown, unfortunately, that the diets of older people tend to be lower in vitamin C, vitamin B_{12}, folate, vitamin D, iron, potassium and dietary fibre than they should be.

Some older people find that their appetite decreases and they may begin to lose their sense of taste. It is very important to have regular mealtimes, even if you are alone, and to try to buy and prepare foods that you enjoy, even if they are not the healthiest of foods. Some people find that they put on weight as they grow older. This is usually because they are less active, so the body no longer uses all the food that the person has grown accustomed to eating and instead converts it to fat. Elderly people can benefit from gentle, regular exercise. It can help stimulate the appetite, keep muscles healthy and flexible, and help to prevent bones thinning and becoming brittle.

In particular, a regular intake of vitamin C should be ensured, because vitamin C plays an important role in protecting against infection and promoting rapid healing of wounds. If an elderly person is confined indoors or is unable to get out into the sunshine very often, it may be worthwhile considering a vitamin D supplement.

It is now thought that we are born with a reserve of vitamin B_{12} in our bodies, which can help prevent deficiency for a long time. If an elderly person has been eating a diet that is low in vitamin B_{12} for many years, he or she may have exhausted this reserve and so will gradually become deficient without realising it. If you think that you may have a deficiency, your doctor can easily perform a blood test for you.

It is important to keep up a good dietary fibre intake, because this can help prevent constipation and also protects against varicose veins. It is unwise, though, to take bran because it can cause digestive upsets. It is far better to eat wholefoods that include dietary fibre along with a variety of other useful nutrients. If you are increasing the amount of fibre in your diet, you should also be increasing your fluid intake. Although it is important not to get into the habit of drinking tea with meals, because this can hinder the body's absorption of iron from the food.

Many homes for the elderly now offer vegetarian meals, and in many areas meals-on-wheels services also offer a vegetarian choice.

acorn squash   The large fruit of a **squash** plant with a hard, dark green or deep gold rind and pulpy, pale orange flesh. The acorn squash is the most common **winter squash**. They are at their best in the autumn; select heavy fruits with glossy skin, and avoid discoloured ones with soft spots. They may be kept for up to a month if stored in a cool dark place.

PREPARATION: acorn squash is best cooked baked and unpeeled. Although the flesh may be parboiled first if preferred.

USES: if prepared whole, serve in halves or slices with the seeds scooped out and filled with a **nut**-based stuffing. Alternatively, the flesh can be served in chunks or puréed, spiced or sweetened.

additive   A natural or artificial substance that manufacturers add to foods to improve appearance, consistency and palatability, to extend shelf life, and as an aid in processing methods. Some vegetarians prefer to avoid processed foods that contain additives, where possible. Natural additives may be derived from animals and as such may be unsuitable for a vegan and vegetarian diet. Named additives that may be unsuitable for a vegetarian diet include **cochineal**, pepsin, **gelatine**, **glycerine**, **hydrolysed proteins**, **lecithin** and **rennet**. See also **E numbers**.

aduki or **adzuki bean**   A small, reddish-brown, round **bean** (a **pulse**) of an Asian plant, which has a

1

delicious, sweet flavour. Aduki beans are easier to digest than some larger beans and are one of the preferred beans in **macrobiotic diets**. The dry beans should be stored in a sealed container in a cool place, and carefully sorted to remove any small stones before use.

PREPARATION: soak for one hour in boiling water or overnight in cold water. Rinse and then boil hard for 10 minutes. Then simmer for approximately 30 minutes or until tender. It is essential to boil the beans in order to destroy toxic **lectins** and **phytic acid**.

USES: aduki beans may be used in a variety of dishes, and are especially good in stews, pies and **pasta** dishes. They can also be mashed and shaped into 'burgers'.

agar (also called **agar-agar** or **kanten**) A substance extracted from **seaweed**, usually **kelp**, that can be used as an alternative gelling agent to **gelatine**. Because it is made from seaweed agar is rich in **iodine**. It is available either as a light grey powder or as sun-dried flakes. Agar is also used as the base of several commercial gelling preparations. It should be stored in a cool dry place.

PREPARATION: agar may be prepared using water, stock or vegetable or fruit juice. Either follow the directions on the packet, or add two teaspoons of agar to 600 ml (1 pint) of liquid.

Bring the mixture to the boil and allow it to simmer for three minutes.

USES: in sweet and savoury jellies and moulds.

alcohol The intoxicating, colourless liquid derived from the fermentation of sugars. Alcohol is found in **spirits**, **wine**, **beer**, **cider** and other intoxicating drinks. Certain processes involved in the production of some commercial alcoholic drinks, notably clearing the liquid using 'finings', can involve the use of ingredients unacceptable to **vegetarians** such as **gelatine**, **isinglass** or **battery eggs**. At present there is no relevant legislation on labelling of ingredients of alcoholic beverages. Some vegetarians prefer to abstain from alcohol for moral or health reasons.

alfalfa The tiny seeds of a Eurasian plant. Once allowed to sprout they form fine, crisp shoots, which are highly nutritious, being rich in **protein** (40%) and **vitamins**. Alfalfa is normally sold ready-sprouted and chilled, or you can buy the seeds and germinate them at home as required.

PREPARATION: place the seeds in a jar and cover tightly with a muslin cloth. Rinse and drain the seeds several times each day until the sprouts reach the desired length.

USES: sprouted alfalfa seeds can be incorporated into salads or eaten in sandwiches. Unsprouted seeds can be sprinkled onto prepared dishes.

alligator pear See **avocado pear**.

allspice The small, round **seeds** of a tropical American tree, used as a mild **spice**. Allspice tastes like a mixture of cinnamon, cloves and nutmeg, and is available whole or ground into a brown powder. Store in a cool, dry place.

USES: may be used in cakes and biscuits. Whole allspice berries can be added to a marinade or to a spice bag for mulled wine.

almond The oval-shaped, nut-like seed of a tree of the peach family from West Asia, of which there are two types, bitter and sweet. Almonds have a higher **protein** content than most **nuts**. They are also high in **calcium** and **fats**. They are available whole, blanched, flaked, chopped or ground. They should be stored in a sealed container in a cool place, because they can become rancid if exposed to air due to their fat content, particularly when ground.

PREPARATION: blanched almonds can be split, chopped or ground in a coffee grinder at home.

USES: almonds' sweet taste goes well with sweet and baked foods. Slivered almonds make a decorative garnish. Chopped almonds can be used in nut-roast dishes, and ground almonds can be used as a flavouring and thickening agent.

alpine strawberry The sweet, red **fruit** of the alpine **strawberry** plant. Compared to more common varieties, alpine strawberries are very small and have a pointed shape. Although sweet and aromatic, they are not very juicy and they are not usually grown commercially.

PREPARATION: alpine strawberries are relatively unusual and so are best enjoyed whole and fresh.

USES: small ones may be used as decoration or served in individual pastry tartlets.

amaranth The large, nutritious **seed** of a decorative, ornamental plant of the pigweed family. Amaranth is available as a seed, flour (see **amaranth flour**) or as puffed seeds from specialist outlets. It is **gluten** free and high in **protein**.

PREPARATION: the seeds may be cooked in boiling water as you would a grain.

USES: puffed amaranth may be used as a breakfast cereal.

amaranth flour A gluten-free **flour** derived from ground **amaranth** seeds. It is richer in **protein**, **iron** and **calcium** than **wheat** flour, and is available from some health-foods shops, or from specialist mail order outlets.

USES: it can be used on its own, or mixed with other flours to make breads, baked goods and pastry.

amchoor (also called **mango powder**) An Indian **spice** made by drying and grinding peeled slices of tart, unripe **mango** into a fine powder. It has a sour taste.

5

USES: amchoor can be used to give a sour flavour to savoury pastries, stir-fried vegetables and drinks.

American cress   See **landcress**.

anelli   A variety of **pasta**, shaped into small rings.

animal fats   This term may refer to any dietary **fats** obtained from an animal source. Some **vegetarian** (though no **vegan**) foods, such as **milk** and **cheese**, contain animal fats. However where the term is used in food labelling it will normally refer to fats such as suet and lard. Since these are obtained from animals after slaughter they are not considered suitable for a vegetarian diet. Animal fats contain mainly saturated fats (see **polyunsaturated fats**.

animal rennet   The common name for rennin, which is an enzyme found in the stomachs of young animals, where it assists in the digestion of **milk**. Animal rennet is extracted from the lining of the fourth stomach of slaughtered calves, and is commonly used to coagulate milk as part of the **cheese** manufacturing process. Cheeses made using animal rennet are not considered suitable for vegetarians. However, many vegetarians do eat these, and labelling is not always clear.

Cheeses suitable for strict vegetarians can be made using **microbial rennet**. See also **genetically engineered rennet**.

aniseed The liquorice-flavoured, aromatic **seeds** of the Mediterranean anise plant. It should be purchased in small quantities and stored in a sealed container in a cool, dry place.

PREPARATION: the seeds may be used whole or crushed to help release their flavour.

USES: aniseed may be used as a **spice** in cakes and biscuits or sprinkled onto salads or cooked vegetables. It may also be steeped in boiling water to make a tea, which is said to be beneficial to digestion.

antioxidant A substance used in **fats** and **oils**, and thereby in foods containing them, to delay, retard or prevent the development of rancidity or other flavour deterioration due to oxidation. Fats and oils, when they come into contact with oxygen in the air, are oxidized and this makes them go rancid, giving them an 'off' flavour and often causing sickness if eaten. Antioxidants are used in food products, such as butter, margarine, meat products, cakes, biscuits and pastry. Antioxidants are also added to non-fat foods, such as cut fruit to prevent discolouration, again caused by oxidation. **Vitamin E** and **vitamin C** have antioxidant functions in the body and they are also used commercially. Manufacturers also use a number of

7

artificial substances that may cause allergies in some people. Antioxidants as food additives are assigned the **E numbers** E220–E330.

apple Any of a variety of firm-fleshed **fruit** of the apple tree, with thin, green, yellow or red skin, crisp white flesh and a bitter core containing dark seeds. Apples are a popular and easily-obtained source of **potassium**, **vitamin C**, **folic acid** and **dietary fibre**. However, peeling, freezing and processing apples seriously reduces their nutritional value. There are a wide variety of apples available, some sweet and some more tart, which are best used in cooking. Avoid apples with soft patches or bruises. They are best stored in the bottom of the refrigerator, but remove them at least one hour before eating.

PREPARATION: apples may be eaten fresh, or cored and baked, or peeled and puréed. If they are to be eaten unpeeled, first wash thoroughly.

USES: apples are often combined with other fruits in sweet dishes. They also complement cheese, and apple sauce is a pleasant addition to dry, **nut**-based dishes.

apple banana A variety of **banana** that is unusually small and plump. It is a good addition to a child's lunch box.

apple cucumber A small, round, yellow variety of **cucumber** with outstanding juiciness and flavour.

apple juice concentrate See **concentrated fruit juice**.

apricot The small, smooth-skinned **fruit** of the apricot tree, with sweet-tasting orange flesh. Select firm, unwrinkled fruit with a deep colour and avoid any with blemishes or a greenish tinge. Apricots are also available dried, either whole, halved or in chunks. They are a good source of beta carotene (see **carotene**), **potassium** and **dietary fibre**. Look for unsulphured dried apricots and **Hunza apricots**, which are not treated with sulphur dioxide.

PREPARATION: apricots can be eaten fresh, or cooked and puréed. Dried apricots can be chopped and eaten dry, or soaked overnight in fruit juice or water and then used like fresh apricots.

USES: apricots can be used in fruit salads and pies, sweet sauces, jams and chutneys.

arame A variety of **seaweed** obtained from the Pacific Ocean off Japan, which has broad, brown leaves. Its leaves are shredded and become black when dried. Arame as a mild, sweet taste and is rich in **iodine**, **calcium** and **iron**.

PREPARATION: wash thoroughly in two changes of water and then soak for 15 minutes before cooking. During this time the arame should almost double in size. Then bring to the boil and allow to simmer for 20 minutes.

USES: although it can be served as a side vegetable, arame is generally used in combination with other **vegetables** and **cereals** – perhaps as a stuffing mixture. Once cooked it can also be used in salads.

arborio rice See **risotto rice**.

arrowroot The easily-digested **starch** extracted from the root of a plant of West Indian origin. It is sold as a powder and should be stored in a sealed container in a cool, dry place. Arrowroot has no taste of its own and is used as a thickening agent.

PREPARATION: the powder should always be mixed to a paste with a little water before being added to a recipe.

USES: arrowroot can be used to glaze fruit and vegetable flans, and to thicken sauces and milky foods.

artichoke See **globe artichoke**; **Jerusalem artichoke**.

arugula See **rocket**.

asafoetida or **asafetida** A strong-smelling plant resin used as a **spice** in Eastern cookery. It is sold as a yellow or white powder, or as a blackish lump and should be used sparingly. It has a very strong sulphurous 'rotten eggs' smell, which becomes more like the smell of onions when the spice is heated. For this reason it is popular amongst Hindu brahmins and Jains, strict vegetarians who also avoid eating onions and garlic.

USES: asafoetida is used almost exclusively in Indian dishes. In some Indian recipe books it is called *hing*.

ascorbic acid See **vitamin C**.

Asian pear (also called **nashi**) An apple-shaped fruit with pale yellow skin and aromatic flesh. It is an unusual fruit, available in some large supermarkets during the winter and early spring only.

PREPARATION: because the crisp flesh has a unique, refreshing taste, and the flavour is different from that of an apple or a pear, it is best enjoyed fresh and whole.

USES: Asian pears may be lightly poached in red wine for an unusual dessert.

asparagus The succulent stem and leaves of the young asparagus plant. There are two main types of asparagus, green and white, of which there are many varieties.

Asparagus is a seasonal vegetable and home-grown asparagus is only available fresh for a few weeks at the beginning of summer. However, it is imported, especially from the Mediterranean countries, and in most cities it can be bought throughout the year. Look for an even-sized bunch of spears, and do not buy asparagus that is dry and wrinkled or has cracked or woody stems. Open tips are a sign of ageing.

11

Asparagus contains **vitamins A**, **C** and **E**, however, canned asparagus contains very little vitamin C.

PREPARATION: wash and trim stems to an equal length, cutting off any woody parts. Steam or lightly boil until tender; it is best cooked standing upright in bundles. Asparagus should be eaten soon after purchase.

USES: as it is a luxury vegetable, asparagus is best presented on its own with butter, hollandaise sauce or cheese sauce. Its flavour complements eggs and it can be added to quiches and soufflés.

asparagus bean (also called **yard-long bean**) The **seed** and pod of an Oriental bean plant, which can reach a very great length when grown in a warm climate. Asparagus beans are usually available from specialist, Oriental food shops.

PREPARATION: they are best eaten when the pods are about 30 cm long. They may be sliced and then boiled or stir-fried, but become limp if steamed.

USES: as this is an unusual food it should be presented in a separate dish so that its flavour may be fully appreciated.

asparagus pea (also called **winged pea**) The **seed** and pod of a plant related to the vetch. The pods are harvested when they are 3–4 cm long, before they become stringy. The pods have frilly 'wings' and a very distinctive appearance.

PREPARATION: the small pods should be steamed or boiled whole for approximately five minutes.

USES: the asparagus pea makes an interesting vegetable dish, and may also be enjoyed in a vegetable stir-fry. See also **pea**.

aubergine (also called **egg plant**) The egg-shaped fruit of a tropical Asian plant, with a glossy skin which can vary in colour from white through to purple – purple is the most common. Choose firm, shiny fruit, free from any brown spots and store in the refrigerator. Aubergines contain traces of **potassium**, **calcium** and **iron**. They are not always acceptable in a **macrobiotic diet**.

PREPARATION: aubergines are related to the nightshade family and their juice can be bitter. To draw out this bitter juice, sprinkle slices of aubergine with salt, leave for 30 minutes, rinse with cold water and pat dry. Aubergines may also be halved, stuffed with a **nut** mixture and baked.

USES: the traditional dish for aubergines is moussaka, which can be made without meat. Chopped aubergines may be used like sliced **courgettes** in casseroles and are a main ingredient in ratatouille.

avocado pear (also called **alligator pear**) The **fruit** of a tropical American plant, with smooth, green or knobbly, black skin. The fruit should be neither hard nor over soft; an avocado in prime ripeness should give slightly when pressed on the pointed end. A hard, unripe fruit ripens in one to two days at room temperature or in about a week if stored in a refrigerator. Ripe avocados may be kept for three to four days if kept in the salad drawer of a refrigerator.

Avocados are rich in vegetable **oils** and should be used sparingly in a low-Calorie diet. They also contain **B complex vitamins**, **protein** and **vitamin E**.

PREPARATION: avocado pears may be simply halved and the pale green flesh eaten alone or with a salad dressing. Alternatively, they can be baked whole or halved.

USES: raw avocado halves can be stuffed with a **cottage cheese** and fruit mixture. Alternatively, use a nutty mixture and bake, wrapped in foil. Soft avocados can be peeled and puréed to make a chilled soup or a dip served with crudités or used in salads.

babacao A large, bright yellow **fruit**, originally discovered in Ecuador and now grown commercially in New Zealand and Guernsey. The centre of the fruit is hollow with only a few seeds and its skin is edible. Because it is shaped like a marrow, with grooves along its sides, slices of babacao have a decorative flower or star shape.

PREPARATION: wash the fruit and slice thinly.

USES: babacao slices make an attractive addition to a fruit salad or may be used as a garnish.

baby coconut A very tiny **coconut**, which, when shelled, may be eaten whole.

baby food Babies can be successfully weaned on to vegetarian foods, such as fruit and vegetable purées, and smooth-ground **rice** and **lentil** mixtures. There are a number of ready-prepared vegetarian baby foods available, including organic varieties. Because babies need to obtain their **vitamins** and other requirements from a limited amount of food they should not be given food which is too low in **fat** or high in **dietary fibre**, as this may satisfy their hunger but not their nutritional requirements. See INTRODUCTION, SPECIAL NEEDS, BABIES AND YOUNG CHILDREN.

baby sweetcorn The tender, sweet-tasting, yellow kernels of unripe **maize**, which have been harvested very early. Sweetcorn is rich in **vitamin A**, **dietary fibre**, **vitamin E** and some **trace elements**.
  PREPARATION: baby sweetcorn can be eaten raw, either whole or halved lengthways. Alternatively, the cobs can be stir-fried or steamed.
  USES: baby sweetcorn features in Chinese, Japanese and Thai cuisine. It makes a colourful addition to a vegetable stir-fry, a sweet and sour dish or a clear vegetable soup. It may also be used raw in salads.

baked beans Baked **haricot beans** canned in tomato sauce. Baked beans may constitute a staple, convenience food in a vegetarian or vegan diet. They are rich in **starch**, **protein**, **dietary fibre** and **iron**. However, they are also often high in refined **sugar salt**.

PREPARATION: haricot beans may be baked at home. Soak them overnight, then place in a casserole dish with a tomato mixture and allow to bake in a low oven (140°C/275°F/Gas 1) for several hours.

USES: as a quick and nutritious vegetable side dish, or, in the traditional manner, hot on wholemeal toast.

baking A method of cooking in the oven, using high temperatures but no water or **fat** (other than fat that may be an ingredient of the foods being baked). In the process no **vitamins** are lost by **leaching** into the cooking water, but some vitamins (**riboflavin**, **thiamin** and **vitamin C**) may be destroyed or depleted by the high temperatures.

Vegetarian foods that may be baked include cakes and breads, vegetables such as baking potatoes, or stuffed peppers and fruits such as baked apples.

baking powder A white powder, containing a mixture of sodium bicarbonate, **starch** and an acidic substance, usually cream of tartar. It is used as a substitute raising agent for **yeast** in baking cakes and bread. At high temperatures, the reaction between the sodium bicarbonate and the cream of tartar releases carbon dioxide gas, which forms tiny bubbles within the dough, causing it to rise and giving it a light, spongy texture when cooked. Baking powder is predominantly an alkaline preparation, and it may cause losses of some **micronutrients**, such as **riboflavin**, **vitamin B_{12}** and **pantothenic acid**, that tend to be destroyed by high temperatures in alkaline conditions, .

balsamic vinegar A rich, dark **vinegar** with a slightly sweet taste made in Italy from **grape** juice. It is produced by a traditional process, involving ageing in wooden barrels, and for this reason it is an expensive vinegar which is best used in dishes where its full flavour will be appreciated.

bamboo shoot The crisp, young stem of bamboo grass, usually sold canned in water, although fresh bamboo shoots are considered superior in taste and texture. Bamboo shoots have a high water content, but they also contain **zinc**, **magnesium** and **dietary fibre**.

PREPARATION: canned bamboo shoots have been boiled before packing, and consequently need little or no further cooking; though they should be rinsed.

Fresh bamboo shoots contain a bitter poison, hydrocyanic acid, that must be destroyed before eating. Strip the leaves and remove the woody base of the shoot, then cut the remainder into bite-sized pieces and boil hard for 10 minutes.

USES: freshly-boiled shoots can be served as a side vegetable or allowed to cool, perhaps marinaded, and served with a salad.

banana The crescent-shaped **fruit** of any of a variety of tropical, palm-like trees. They have thick, yellow, inedible skins and starchy, off-white flesh with a sweet taste. Bananas are a good source of **dietary fibre** and contain **potassium**. They also contain large amounts of **starch**, which turns to sugar as they ripen. Bananas are not, as it is often supposed, fattening, but they do contain more Calories than most fruits.

Buy bananas that are on the point of ripening from green to yellow and avoid any with large black patches. Allow a few brown speckles to appear on the skin before eating. They are best kept in the fruit bowl and should never be kept in the refrigerator. They are also available sun-dried or baked into crisp chips.

PREPARATION: always peel and discard the skins. They may then be sliced, mashed or puréed. They do not need to be cooked, but may be baked whole or sliced and fried.

USES: bananas can be added to fruit salads, although once sliced they do not keep well, quickly turning brown. Mashed or puréed bananas may be used to sweeten a glass of **milk** or **soya milk**, or as a natural sweetener in cake mixtures. Fried bananas can be served as a side dish with Indian meals, and hot, baked bananas can be served with

cream or **concentrated soya milk** and **honey** as a rich dessert.

banana flour A **gluten**-free **flour** derived from **bananas**, available from some health-food shops, or from specialist mail-order outlets.

USES: it can be used on its own or mixed with other flours to make breads, baked goods and pastry.

barley A **cereal** used commercially to make beer and whisky. Barley is sold unrefined, as **pot barley**, or milled, as **pearl barley**. Barley is not especially high in any vitamins or minerals compared to other grains. However, unrefined it is a useful source of **protein**, **dietary fibre** and some **B complex vitamins**. It is relatively low in Calories and very easy to digest.

PREPARATION: pot barley should be cooked in boiling water for around two hours until it becomes tender. It has a chewy texture, whereas pearl barley tends to become soft and watery.

USES: pot barley is traditionally added to soups and casseroles. Pearl barley may be used in milk puddings and, because it is easy to digest, is suitable for convalescents. See also **barley flour**.

barley flour A **flour** ground from wholegrain barley, which contains a small amount of **gluten**.

USES: combined with, or as a replacement for, wheat flour in baking.

barn egg (also called **farm egg**) It is important
to note that barn **eggs** are not **free-range eggs**. The
hens are kept in large barns in which there are
perches, and the maximum number of hens per
square metre is 25. There is no access to the outside and natural light is limited. The barn system is
an intensive farming system. See also **battery egg**.

bartlet pear A juicy, smooth-skinned variety of
pear which is popular in America although it is
seasonally available during the autumn only.

basil The aromatic leaves of a Eurasian plant
used as a **herb**. It may be purchased fresh, dried,
freeze-dried or as a small plant for the kitchen
windowsill. Fresh basil should be used as soon as
possible after purchase. Dried basil should be
stored in a sealed container and replaced if it
begins to lose its aroma.
  PREPARATION: fresh basil should be rinsed
before use. The large, soft leaves are best torn by
hand to release their full flavour.
  USES: basil is traditionally combined with
tomatoes and features in many Italian and Mediterranean dishes. It also goes well with **egg** and
green-leaf salads, and may be used to flavour oils
and marinades. Combine it with **garlic**, **nuts**, **Parmesan cheese** and **olive oil** to make pesto.

basmati rice A variety of **rice** available either
white or brown. It has exceptionally long grains, a

fragrant aroma and a distinctive taste. It is regarded as a high-quality speciality rice, and is sometimes described as the 'Prince of Rice'.

PREPARATION: cook 250 g of white basmati rice in 450 ml of boiling water for 10 minutes on the hob or in a medium oven for 35 minutes. The same amount of brown basmati rice should be cooked in 600 ml of boiling water for 25 minutes or in a medium oven for 50 minutes.

USES: as an accompaniment to curries and to make Indian-style biryani and pilau dishes.

batata A variety of **sweet potato** with a red skin and a fat, tapered shape, grown in South America and the Caribbean. The name *batata* is the origin of the word 'potato'.

batavian endive (also called **escarole**) The most common broad-leafed variety of **endive**.

battery egg An **egg** produced by a hen housed in a battery cage. Although in principle eggs of all kinds are suitable for vegetarians, many vegetarians prefer to avoid eating battery eggs, as the battery system is considered inhumane. See also **barn egg**; **free-range egg**.

bay The leaves of a species of Mediterranean laurel tree, used fresh or dried as a **herb** to give flavour to foods. Dried leaves should have a fresh green colour and strong scent. Dull and faded leaves should be discarded.

PREPARATION: bay leaves are not eaten but are added to foods during cooking to add flavour. They may also be powdered, or tied into a muslin sachet with other herbs to make a bouquet garni.

USES: the flavour of bay goes well with **carrots** and **cabbage** and can brighten an otherwise uninteresting dish. A leaf may also be used in cooking Italian-style **tomato** sauces or **lentil** dishes.

B complex vitamins   A group of water-soluble vitamins which are known to work together in the body, although they have different functions. The B complex vitamins are: **thiamin** (vitamin B_1), **riboflavin** (vitamin B_2), **niacin** (vitamin B_3), **pantothenic acid** (vitamin B_5), **vitamin B_6** (pyridoxine), **vitamin B_{12}** (cyanocobalamin), **biotin** (vitamin H) and **folic acid**.

These vitamins often occur together in the same foods, and useful vegetarian sources of B complex vitamins include **dairy products**, **pulses**, green vegetables, wholegrain cereals and **brewer's yeast**. Vitamin B_{12} is found in few, if any, plant sources, but vegetarians obtain an adequate intake from dairy foods and **eggs**. Many vegan foods are supplemented with vitamin B_{12}.

bean   The edible seed or young seed pod of leguminous plants. Beans are an important part of a vegetarian diet. They are a good source of **protein**, especially if combined with whole grains or **dairy products**. They also offer **carbohydrate**, **dietary**

fibre and some **B complex vitamins**. It is best to buy dried beans from a shop that has a speedy turnover.

PREPARATION: except for **split peas** and **lentils**, all dried beans need to be soaked in water – usually overnight – before cooking. They should then be well rinsed and cooked in fresh water. Beans should be thoroughly boiled for 10 minutes to destroy any toxins. They can then be simmered until soft. Beans may be cooked in a pressure cooker, but they must be boiled first before being cooked in a slow cooker.

USES: beans have a satisfying mealy texture which gives bulk to a meal. They have a very wide variety of uses. See **aduki bean**; **asparagus bean**; **baked beans**; **bean sprout**; **black bean**; **black-eyed pea**; **black kidney bean**; **borlotti bean**; **broad bean**; **butter bean**; **cannellini bean**; **chickpea**; **cow pea**; **field bean**; **flageolet bean**; **French bean**; **haricot bean**; **kidney bean**; **mung bean**; **pinto bean**; **runner bean**; **soya bean**.

bean curd See **tofu**.

bean sprout Any of a variety of **beans** that have been soaked for several days to produce a crisp white sprout. The most commonly available are sprouted **mung beans**, but all kinds of beans can be successfully sprouted at home. The process significantly improves the nutritional value of beans. Bean sprouts are rich in **protein**, **vitamin A**, **vitamin C** and the **B complex vitamins**.

23

Pre-sprouted beans are sold chilled in plastic bags. Check before buying that they are not going soft and brown. They should be stored in an air-tight bag or jar in the refrigerator and used soon after purchase.

PREPARATION: **aduki beans**, **chickpeas**, whole **lentils**, mung beans and **soya beans** can be sprouted at home. Soak them in water overnight, then rinse and drain them. Place them in a large, wide-necked jar and cover the jar with a piece of muslin fastened with an elastic band. Sprouts grown in the dark are high in **thiamin**, and sprouts grown in the light are high in vitamin C. Rinse the sprouts in ice-cold water immediately before use.

USES: bean sprouts are delicate and should be only lightly cooked or eaten raw. They may be used in many Oriental dishes, stir-fried or lightly steamed. They may also be mixed in with **bread** dough and **burger** mixes and used in salads and sandwiches.

beefsteak tomato A very large, fleshy variety of **tomato**. Although it may lack some flavour it is ideal for slicing and also for stuffing.

beer An alcoholic drink usually made with malted **barley**, yeast and hops. Cask-conditioned beers are cleared by adding **isinglass** (a fish by-product); this sinks to the bottom of the casks, but it may mean that such beers are unsuitable for strict vegetarians. Bottled, naturally-conditioned beers, canned beers and keg beers, however, do not go through this process.

beetroot The dark purple root of a variety of beet plant. Beetroot can be purchased preserved in jars of **vinegar**, pre-cooked or raw. Cooked and raw beetroots should look firm and free from any obvious damage. Small beetroots are sweeter than large ones. Raw beetroot should be stored in a cool, dark place, and cooked beetroot should be refrigerated.

PREPARATION: to cook beetroots, first wash them in cold water, but do not remove the leaf-stalks or the root. Do not damage the skin because this may allow the juice to leach out during cooking and impair the flavour. Boil for between one and two hours. When cooked the skin can be rubbed off. Alternatively, bake whole beetroots in a medium oven for up to two hours. Cooked beetroot can be served hot or cold, or it may be pickled.

USES: beetroot is most commonly used to give colour to salads. However, it can be used as a side vegetable or to make borsch – a traditional Eastern-European soup.

Belgian endive See **chicory**.

ber (also called **Chinese apple**, **Indian plum** or **jujube**) A small, brown, oval-shaped **fruit** from

Asia, with crisp, white flesh and a refreshing taste.
It is not widely available, but it can be bought
from some specialist shops during winter.

PREPARATION: usually eaten raw.
USES: add to an exotic fruit cocktail.

berry   Any of various small, soft, edible **fruits**.
See **alpine strawberry**; **blackberry**; **blueberry**; **boysenberry**; **cloudberry**; **dewberry**; **elderberry**; **gooseberry**; **juniper berry**; **loganberry**; **mulberry**;
raspberry; **rowanberry**; **strawberry**; **sunberry**;
tayberry.

besan   See **gram flour**.

beta carotene   See **carotene**.

bilberry   See **blueberry**.

biotin (also called **vitamin H** or **co-enzyme
R**)   One of the **B complex vitamins** involved in the
metabolism and energy release from nutrients. It
is synthesized by intestinal bacteria in adults and
is also obtained from the diet. Vegetarian sources
include brown **rice**, **nuts**, **brewer's yeast** and **egg**
yolks (cooked without the white). A daily intake
of 150–200 µg is regarded as adequate.

Raw eggs contain a **protein** called avidin in the
white, which binds to biotin, making it unavailable for absorption. Avadin is destroyed, however, by the heat of cooking.

bio-yoghurt See **live yoghurt**.

black bean (also called **black kidney bean**) A
shiny, black **pulse** related to the **red kidney bean**,
which has a similar but slightly larger shape.
Black beans are only available dried in this country, and are cooked in the same way and can be
used in the same recipes as red kidney beans.

blackberry The black or purple **fruit** of the
bramble. Fresh blackberries have a limited season
– late summer to early autumn – but they may be
purchased frozen and canned. Blackberries can be
picked from the wild, but do so with care,
avoiding polluted roadsides and always washing
the fruit thoroughly before eating. Blackberries
are a good source of **vitamin C** and **vitamin E**, and
also contain **carotene** and **iron**.
  PREPARATION: to preserve the nutritional content, blackberries are best eaten fresh. Pull out the
prickly leaf crown and white core, and wash the
berries carefully as they are easily damaged.
  USES: perfect blackberries are best served alone
or as part of a special berry dish. Soft or damaged
blackberries can be used in jam or wine making.

black cherry See **cherry**.

blackcurrant The small, black **fruit** of a temperate shrub, with thin, shiny black skin and juicy,
green flesh. They are delicate fruits and do not

27

travel well, so availability is limited and seasonal. Fresh, raw blackcurrants are a particularly good source of **vitamin C** and they also contain **potassium**, **iron**, **carotene**, **biotin** and some **vitamin E**. They are best eaten soon after purchase.

PREPARATION: washing may damage the fruit and removal of the tiny stems is a matter of taste. They may be left on if the fruit is to be puréed.

USES: blackcurrants can be stewed or baked in a pie or tart, or eaten raw. They also make good jams and jellies, and sweet or tart sauces.

black-eyed pea (also called **black-eyed bean** or **cowpea**) A beige-coloured **pulse** with a distinctive black mark or eye at the point where it was originally joined to the pod. Black-eyed peas have a sweet flavour, similar to that of the garden pea, and are sold dried.

PREPARATION: black-eyed peas must be soaked overnight, rinsed well, brought to the boil in fresh water for 10 minutes and then allowed to simmer for around 30 minutes. They are one of the fastest-cooking beans and can also be cooked without pre-soaking, which takes slightly longer.

USES: the colour of black-eyed peas makes them an interesting addition to a cold-bean salad or a hot-bean casserole. They can also be mashed to make a paté or **burgers**.

black kidney bean See **black bean**.

black onion seed (also called **kalonji** or **nigella**) The small, irregularly-shaped black seeds of a plant that grows wild in India. It is not related to the **onion** family, but the seeds resemble onion seeds.

USES: the seeds are added whole or ground as a **spice**, usually to Indian dishes and stir-fries. They can also be used in pickles.

black pepper A hot-tasting powder made by grinding whole, sun-dried **peppercorns**. It is available as a powder or as whole peppercorns, which may be ground as required in a pepper mill.

USES: black pepper is commonly used as a **spice** to give a hot taste to a variety of foods.

blackstrap molasses A particularly dark variety of **molasses**.

black treacle A dark viscous syrup obtained as a by-product during the refining of **sugar** crystals. Because it is high in **sugars** it is used as a sweetener. However, it does contain **potassium**, **calcium**, **magnesium** and **iron**.

USES: black treacle has a distinctive taste and should be used where this will be appreciated. It may be used in cakes, breads and rich casseroles, and also to make toffee.

blanching A method of pre-cooking food by immersing it in boiling water for a very short time.

Because the food is cooked for only a brief period, the nutrient loss is minimal. Manufacturers blanch ingredients in the preparation of some canned and frozen foods. Vegetables that are to be frozen at home must be blanched first in order to destroy enzymes and to preserve the colour and flavour of the vegetable. **Fruits** (e.g. **tomatoes**) and **nuts** (e.g. **almonds**) can be blanched to make it easier to peel away the skin. **Peppers** are often blanched before they are stuffed and baked. Some vegetables (e.g. **French beans** or **mangetout**) may be blanched and then chilled for use in salads.

blood orange　A variety of **orange** with red flesh which yields a red juice, making it an interesting choice for a fruit salad.

blueberry (also called **bilberry** or **whortleberry**)　A small, blue-black berry of a North American shrub, which can also be found wild in the UK. The fruits are sweet with a natural, grey bloom. Blueberries should be stored in the refrigerator, and any decay spreads rapidly, so remove any bruised berries.

PREPARATION: if soft, blueberries can be eaten raw. Otherwise, they can be stewed or baked in a pie or tart.

USES: berry salads go well with liqueurs and chocolate. Blueberries can be used to top cheesecakes, made into traditional muffins, used to flavour vinegars or made into jam.

blue cheese   A cheese with veins of blue mould (such as Stilton or Roquefort), which is almost always made with **animal rennet**. Blue cheeses have a strong flavour and can be used to make a tasty salad dressing, melted on pizza or in a fondue, or served with a green salad.

boiling   A method of cooking using boiling water (100°C). Some **vitamins** (such as **thiamin**, **pantothenic acid** and **vitamin C**) are destroyed at such a high temperature, while others (such as **niacin**, **riboflavin** and **vitamin B$_{12}$**), along with small amounts of mineral salts may be **leached** into the cooking water. To minimize these losses, food should be boiled for a short time only, using a minimum of water. Where possible this cooking water should be reserved to make a stock, sauce or soup. **Steaming** is a method of cooking vegetables that causes less loss of nutrients.

borecole   See **kale**.

borlotti bean (also called **pink bean**)   A **pulse** related to the **kidney bean** with a pinkish, speckled skin and a bland taste.
   PREPARATION: borlotti beans should be soaked overnight, rinsed thoroughly, brought to the boil in fresh water and simmered for around an hour until tender. They become floury and mealy when cooked, and mash well.

USES: borlotti beans may disintegrate in slow-cooked casseroles and are better mashed to make **burgers** or a paté.

boron A **trace element**.

boysenberry The large red **fruit** of a type of bramble, which is a cross between a **loganberry** and a **raspberry**. The flavour is like that of a wild **blackberry**.

PREPARATION: wash and serve or purée.

USES: although larger, boysenberries may be used as an alternative to raspberries in recipes.

braising A method of cooking usually applied to meat, but which can also be employed to cook some vegetarian foods. The food is lightly fried and then allowed to simmer in a small amount of liquid in a closed container. The frying, which enhances the flavour of the food, may cause small losses of those **vitamins** that are unstable at high temperatures (e.g. **thiamin**, **pantothenic acid** and **vitamin C**). However, this cooking method reduces the loss of nutrients through **leaching** because the food is served in the liquid in which it is cooked. Mixtures of vegetables, such as **leeks** and **carrots**, can be successfully cooked in this way.

bran The fibrous outer husk of **cereals**. The most common bran available is **wheat** bran, but bran can be taken from any cereal. It can be purchased coarse or fine milled and is a very good source of **dietary fibre**. Bran is a particularly good source of soluble fibre, which is thought to help reduce raised blood pressure. It should be stored in an airtight container and purchased in small quantities.

PREPARATION: bran can be stirred into foods and added to flour. It should be used with caution as it may cause digestive problems. Uncooked bran is also thought to inhibit the absorption of **zinc**, **calcium** and **iron** in the diet due to the presence of **phytic acid**. For this reason it is best to try to obtain fibre through a wholefood diet. Vegetarian diets are often very high in natural fibre.

USES: use in bread and biscuit making.

brazil nut   The crescent-shaped **nut** of a tropical, South American tree with a woody, brown shell and off-white kernel. Brazil nuts can be purchased whole, shelled or chopped. They are rich in **protein**, **zinc** and **B complex vitamins**. However, they also have a high **fat** content, which means that they are high in Calories. Shelled nuts should be stored in an airtight container.

PREPARATION: unshelled nuts can be cracked as needed and then chopped or ground at home.

USES: brazil nuts have a moist texture which is pleasant in a **nut roast** or nut paté. Ground nuts can be added to sweet pastry and biscuits.

bread Any of a great variety of foods made from **flour** dough. Most bread is made from **wheat** flour, sometimes with **oats** and **wholegrains** added. It can also be made from a variety of other flours, such as **rye**, **barley** and **corn meal**. A range of breads originating from other countries are now readily available in most supermarkets and bakers' shops, including: fresh or frozen French sticks and Italian-style garlic bread; **pitta bread** made with either white or brown flour; poppadums, naan bread and chapatis, often made with **herbs** and **spices**; bread baked with olive oil and American corn bread.

Bread is a good source of complex **carbohydrates** and **protein**, and is a moderately good source of a range of **minerals**. The **phytic acid** in the grain is destroyed by the action of the yeast, so the absorption of minerals such as **zinc** is not impaired. Bread made from wholemeal flour is a particularly rich source of **B complex vitamins**, **folic acid** and **biotin**.

PREPARATION: if making bread at home, experiment by adding herbs or spices, rolled oats or whole wheat grains, copped **nuts**, **seeds**, or even **dried fruits** and chopped, cooked vegetables (such as **onion**) to the dough. Unleavened breads, such as soda bread, are quicker to make than yeasted bread, but they do not store as well and contain phytic acid.

USES: wholemeal bread and rolls make very nutritious sandwiches and toast. The traditional

baked beans on toast is a simple and protein-rich meal.

breadfruit   A large, melon-shaped **fruit** with a thick, brown skin and starchy, sweetish flesh. It is occasionally available at specialist shops, but it does not store well.

PREPARATION: the flesh can be cut into cubes or slices and boiled, baked or fried. It can also be baked whole and then stuffed.

USES: cooked breadfruit can be served as a side vegetable with an ethnic-style meal or cooked in a stew or soup. It can also be sliced and made into chips or crisps.

brewer's yeast   The variety of **yeast** used in brewing **beer**. This by-product of the brewing process has a high nutrient content and is sold as a food supplement in flake, tablet or powder form. It is a rich source of **B complex vitamins**.

USES: the powder has a distinctive yeasty flavour. It can be stirred into fruit or vegetable juice to make an energy-boosting drink.

broad bean (also called **English bean**, **fava bean** or **horse bean**)   The pale green seed of a Eurasian bean plant. Broad beans can be eaten as a fresh **vegetable** or dried beans can be soaked and cooked. Broad beans contain **starch** and **protein**, **dietary fibre** and a variety of **minerals**.

PREPARATION: broad beans can contain small quantities of **phytic acid** and **lectins** which must be destroyed by boiling. Small, fresh pods can be cooked whole and then sliced. Mature beans should be taken out of the pod and boiled for about 10 minutes. If the skins are still tough, they can be rubbed off.

Dried beans should be soaked overnight, rinsed well and brought to the boil for 10 minutes. They may then be simmered for approximately one and a half hours.

USES: fresh broad beans can be served as a vegetable, or in a soup. Cooked dried beans can be added to soups or salads.

broccoli (also called **calabrese**) The flower head of a plant related to **cabbage** and **cauliflower**. Its name comes from the Italian word for 'cabbage sprout'. There are several varieties, including sprouting varieties with many purple, white or green shoots and those that produce one, large closed head, similar to a cauliflower. Broccoli should be eaten before the tiny green buds begin to turn into yellow flowers. It is rich in **calcium**, **potassium**, **carotene** and **B complex vitamins**.

PREPARATION: trim the stems, and halve lengthways any particularly thick stems. Steam or boil until tender. Alternatively, **blanch** and add to stir-fries and salads. An acidic marinade will cause broccoli to yellow.

USES: as a side vegetable, broccoli can be served buttered or with a sauce. It goes well with **cheese**, and may be used in a quiche.

brown lentil   A dark brown variety of **lentil** slightly smaller than the **continental lentil**. They retain their shape and texture well in cooking and have a more intense flavour than other lentils.

PREPARATION: soak overnight, rinse and bring to the boil in fresh water. Boil for 10 minutes and then simmer for 30 minutes until soft. Alternatively, brown lentils can be cooked without soaking. Again they must be boiled for 10 minutes and should then be simmered for an hour to an hour and a half.

USES: brown lentils may be used in any recipe which requires continental lentils. They are particularly good in vegetable Cornish pasties, shepherds pie and **burgers**.

brown rice   See **rice**.

brown seaweed   See **kelp**.

Brussels sprout   The small bud of a variety of **cabbage**. Brussels sprouts should be firm, not soft, and their leaves should not be turning yellow. They may be stored in the refrigerator. They are a good source of **vitamin C**, also **dietary fibre**, **protein**, **carotene** and **folic acid**.

PREPARATION: trim the stalk and cut a cross into the base. Wash and remove damaged leaves. Boil or steam.

USES: as a side vegetable or puréed in a soup, chopped in a casserole or grated in a salad.

buckwheat The seeds of the buckwheat plant, used as a **grain** or ground into a flour. Buckwheat contains **starch**, **protein**, **dietary fibre**, **potassium**, **iron**, **zinc**, **B complex vitamins** and **vitamin E**. It is available as crushed and hulled grains called groats or as whole roasted grains. Both the roasted grains and the traditional dish made with them are known as **kasha**. **Pasta** made from buckwheat is also available.

PREPARATION: dry roast in a pan, carefully add water and cook like **rice**.

USES: as a side dish, in a grain salad, to stuff vegetables or in any rice-based dish. Buckwheat flour is traditionally used to make Russian *blinis*, a kind of pancake.

buckwheat flour A **gluten**-free **flour** made from **buckwheat**.

USES: it can be used on its own or mixed with other flours to make breads, baked goods and pastry.

bulgar, **bulgur** or **bulghur** A form of **wheat** that has been hulled and **parboiled** to make the grains easier to cook and the texture lighter. The nutritional content is similar to wheat.

PREPARATION: since they are partially cooked, the grains need only be boiled in water for a further 15–20 minutes.

USES: bulgar is normally cooked and eaten in place of rice in salads, as a side dish or as a stuffing for vegetables. It is the main ingredient of the Lebanese salad tabbouleh.

bullock's heart A variety of **custard apple** with a heart shape and bland taste.

burger In general the term burger refers to a meat patty. However, vegetarian burgers are available ready-made (fresh, chilled or frozen) or as dried mixtures. They may consist largely of vegetables, of **pulses** or of **textured vegetable protein**. Some ready-made vegetarian burgers are manufactured using **battery eggs**, which may not be considered suitable for vegetarians. Burger mixes are versatile and can be made up using eggs or water, along with a variety of optional extras.

butter A fatty, whitish-yellow paste made from churning the **cream** of cows' **milk**. Butter is high in saturated fats (see **polyunsaturated fats**) and also contains **vitamin A** and **vitamin D**, provided that the cows have not been confined indoors. It is available either salted or unsalted.

USES: butter can be used as a spread or in cooking. It is good melted on hot plain vegetables.

butter bean (also called **lima bean** or **marrow bean**) The flat, pale yellow seed of a variety of bean of North American origin. They are available dried or canned. The beans are soft and floury when cooked.

39

PREPARATION: butter beans can contain small amounts of **phytic acid** and **lectins** which must be destroyed. Soak dried beans overnight, rinse well and bring to the boil in fresh water. Boil for 10 minutes, then simmer for around an hour.

USES: butter beans can be served as a side vegetable, perhaps in a sauce. They can be added to casseroles, **pasta** sauces or salads.

butterhead lettuce A popular variety of **lettuce** with smooth, rounded leaves.

buttermilk The sour watery liquid left when **butter** has been separated from **cream**. Manufactured buttermilk, often known as cultured buttermilk, is made from **skimmed milk** with a culture added to make it thicker. Buttermilk is more watery than **milk**, but it does provide **protein**, **calcium**, **iron** and **B complex vitamins**, and has fewer Calories than milk.

USES: buttermilk can be used in fruity milkshakes. It can also be used in baking and in sauces, much like milk.

butter nut A variety of **walnut** from North America, with a thick shell. It is not widely available outside the US.

butternut squash One of the most popular and widely available of the **winter squashes**. It is shaped like a large, flat-bottomed pear and has smooth, yellow skin. See also **acorn squash**.

button mushroom A variety of **mushroom** with a small, white, closed cap under which the gills are still hidden.

button onion A very tiny variety of **onion**, which may be used whole or halved in casseroles or on vegetable kebabs.

cabbage The large leafy bud of a variety of European plant. It has tightly packed, crisp, white, green or purple leaves, or more loosely packed green leaves that may have a wrinkled texture. Cabbage is a good source of **potassium**, **vitamin C** and **folic acid**, especially if eaten raw. Green cabbage also contains **carotene** and **calcium**. Buy according to the season.

PREPARATION: cabbage can be boiled, or shredded and stir-fried or it may be eaten raw.

USES: cabbage may be used in a variety of ways, as a straightforward side vegetable or grated raw into coleslaw. Large, boiled cabbage leaves may be stuffed, in the same way as **vine leaves**. It can also be used to make bubble and squeak or fried and as an ingredient in potato cakes. See **red cabbage**; **savoy cabbage**; **white salad cabbage**. See also **kohlrabi**.

cactus fruit See **prickly pear**.

caffeine An organic substance naturally present in **coffee, tea** and the cola nut, originally used in cola drinks. A daily intake of 250 mg of caffeine (equivalent to five cups of tea or coffee) is usually sufficient to have a stimulant effect. At greater intakes it may accelerate the heart rate, cause a jittery feeling in the muscles, lightheadedness and sleeplessness in some people. It also has a diuretic effect. Many people who are vegetarian for health reasons prefer to drink decaffeinated tea and coffee, or **herbal teas**.

calabaza pumpkin See **pumpkin**.

calabrese See **broccoli**.

calcium The most abundant **mineral** in the body, found almost entirely in the bones and teeth. Calcium also controls nerve impulses and muscle contractions. The best natural sources of calcium are **milk, cheese** and **yoghurt**. White **flour** and some **soya milks** are fortified with calcium. Dark green vegetables are good sources, but some, such as **spinach**, contain **oxalic acid** – an acid that interferes with calcium absorption. The calcium in **nuts** and **pulses** is also not well absorbed because of the presence of **phytic acid**.

Calorie A unit of heat, originally defined as the quantity of heat required to raise the temperature of 1 g of water by 1°C. The body's energy requirements and the energy value of food are measured in kilocalories (1000 calories; abbreviation kcal) or kilojoules. If Calorie is written with a captial C it is equivalent to a kilocalorie.

camomile or **chamomile tea**   A variety of **herbal tea** that is widely commercially available. Camomile tea is claimed to have a sedative effect and to aid sleep, as well as calming the digestive system. It is available as a dried mixture or in ready-prepared tea bags. It is not made with **milk**, but may be sweetened to taste.

cannellini bean   A white **pulse** related to the **kidney bean**, but slightly larger. It has a pleasant flavour and mealy texture.
PREPARATION: soak overnight, rinse thoroughly and bring to the boil in fresh water. Boil for 10 minutes, then simmer for up to one and a half hours until soft.
USES: cannellini beans are interchangeable with **red kidney beans**, **haricot beans** and **butter beans** in recipes.

cannelloni   A variety of **pasta** shaped as large tubes, which can be stuffed with a **tomato**, **cheese**, **spinach** or **nut** stuffing and baked in a sauce.

cantaloupe or **cantaloup melon**   A variety of **melon** with a round shape and scaly, dull-yellow skin. The flesh is orange, sweet and fragrant.

43

cape gooseberry (also called **physalis**) A small, round, golden **fruit** from South Africa, which is sometimes available in the second half of the year. The flesh is sweet but the many edible pips have a sharp taste.

PREPARATION: peel and eat whole or sliced.

USES: a novelty, best served fresh and uncooked as a special dish, rather than lost in a pie or pudding. They are also good in jams and jellies.

caper The small wrinkled seed of a trailing, Mediterranean shrub. They are sun-dried and then preserved in brine. Capers have a sharp taste and should be used in moderation.

USES: add to savoury dishes and sauces.

capsicum The family name for several varieties of peppers.

carambola See **star fruit**.

caraway seed The long, thin, curved seed of a variety of Eurasian shrub. They have a tangy taste and are used as a **spice**. It is claimed that they aid digestion. They should be stored in an airtight container in a cool place.

USES: to decorate bread, add to cakes, or sprinkle onto cooked cabbage and other vegetables.

carbohydrate Any of a number of organic compounds made up of carbon, hydrogen and oxygen, which are converted by the body into energy. If that energy is not used by the body, whether because too much is eaten or too little exercise is taken, it is stored in the body as fat. The main categories of carbohydrates are **sugars**, **starch** and **dietary fibre**.

The body uses disaccharides (complex sugars), such as **sucrose**, **lactose** and **maltose**, to make monosaccharides, such as **glucose**, **fructose** and galactose. Sugars are mainly available from plant foods, although **milk** does contain some lactose, and meat, such as liver, galactose. Galactose is sometimes known as animal starch.

Starch is found in plant foods and is available refined (e.g. **white** rice or **white** flour) or unrefined (e.g. brown rice or flour). Dietary fibre is not found in animal foods only plants, and consequently a vegetarian diet is typically high in fibre. Foods that contain both starch and fibre are known as complex carbohydrates.

The average UK diet gets 45% of its energy requirements from carbohydrates, but nutritionists recommend that this should be increased to 50%. Sugars are often referred to as 'empty **Calories**' because they provide energy but lack other nutrients. Therefore, it is the consumption of complex carbohydrates which provide energy, dietary fibre and nutrients, that should be increased.

Vegetarian foods rich in complex carbohydrates include wholegrain **cereals**, cereal products (e.g. **pasta** and **bread**), **fruit**, **vegetables** and **pulses**.

cardamom, cardamum or **cardamon** The tiny, black, aromatic seeds of a tropical plant contained in a small, pale green pod, which are sold dried. The seeds are generally used in Indian dishes. They should be stored in a cool dry place.

PREPARATION: whole pods or seeds can be added to dishes during cooking. The seeds may also be crushed to help release their flavour; it is best to do this in small quantities as required.

USES: as well as featuring in Indian and in Scandinavian dishes, cardomoms may be used in **milk** puddings and hot, fruity desserts.

carob (also called **locust bean**) A cocoa (see **cocoa powder**) substitute obtained from grinding the pod of an evergreen Mediterranean tree. Carob looks and tastes similar to cocoa but contains no **caffeine**. It is rich in **calcium**, **iron** and **potassium**, as well as **sugars** and **starch**. Carob is usually sold as a powder, but it is also used commercially to make sugar- and dairy-product-free chocolate substitutes.

USES: although carob powder does not taste exactly like cocoa it can be used in place of cocoa in cakes, desserts and milk shakes.

carotene Any of a number of different substances (alpha-, beta- and gamma-carotene) that have the ability to be converted by the body into

vitamin A (retinol). Carotene has a characteristically bright orange colour, and many good food sources are recognizable by this colour, such as **carrots**, **cantaloupe melons**, **apricots** and **pumpkins**.

Carotene is the major source of vitamin A in **vegan** diets, as retinol is found only in meat, fish, **dairy products** and **eggs**.

carrageen, **carragheen** or **carrageenan** (also called **Irish moss**) A powder made from **seaweed** and used as a gelling agent.

USES: carrageen powder can be stirred into sauces and soups as a thickener. When used to set food it gives a lighter texture than that associated with **agar**. It may also be cooked and eaten as a vegetable.

carrot A long, tapering, orange, **root vegetable**. Carrots are a popular vegetable and available fresh all year. They are rich in **carotene** and also contain **vitamin C** and **B complex vitamins**. Fresh carrots are best purchased young and should be bright-coloured and firm. They should be stored in the refrigerator. They are also available frozen and canned.

PREPARATION: young carrots can be scrubbed, older ones should be scraped or peeled. They can be steamed or boiled, whole, sliced or in pieces. Thin strips (julienne) of carrot can be stir-fried.

USES: young carrots can be served as a side vegetable, with **butter** or a sauce. They can be eaten raw, as crudites or in grated salads. Cut grooves into the sides so that the slices have a decorative flower shape. Carrots are a staple ingredient of casseroles and stews because they readily absorb flavours. They make a good soup and are also used to make carrot cake and some Indian sweets.

casaba melon   A variety of winter **melon** with deeply grooved, yellow rind.

cashew nut   The kidney-shaped **nut** of a tropical, South American tree. Cashews are sold shelled, salted, toasted and chopped. They have a high **fat** content, and also contain **potassium**, **calcium**, **manganese**, **phosphorus**, **niacin**, **folic acid** and a trace of **iron**. They do not store well and should be used soon after purchase.

PREPARATION: cashews can be toasted or dry roasted before use to impart a stronger flavour or may be eaten raw. They can be ground with water to make a **nut milk** or cream to serve with a dessert or fruit.

USES: in **nut roasts**, curries and fruit-and-nut snacks.

cassava (also called **manioc**)   The starchy root of a tropical American plant. Bitter cassava is usually cultivated for the extraction of **tapioca**. Its main nutrient is **starch**. Sweet cassava is more widely available and is eaten as a vegetable.

PREPARATION: bake, boil or slice thinly and fry. Bitter cassava can be poisonous unless correctly prepared.

USES: as a side vegetable.

cassava flour A starchy, **gluten**-free **flour** made from the **cassava** root.

USES: it can be used on its own or mixed with other flours to make breads, baked goods and pastry.

cauliflower The tightly packed, white flower of a variety of **cabbage**. The 'curd' should be creamy white with no brown markings. Cauliflower should be enjoyed as fresh as possible and can be stored in the refrigerator. It contains some **vitamin C**, **potassium** and **B complex vitamins**, but cooking depletes these.

PREPARATION: cauliflower florets can be eaten raw, generally, however, cauliflower is cooked in boiling water or steamed.

USES: as a side vegetable. Cauliflower **cheese** is a classic inexpensive vegetarian meal and raw cauliflower can be used in salads.

cayenne pepper A pungent, bright orange-red **pepper** made from the ground seeds and pods of a variety of **capsicum**. It is used as a **spice**. To preserve the colour, store away from light.

USES: cayenne is often used as decoration sprinkled sparingly on **cheese** dishes.

celeriac The large bulbous white root of a variety of **celery** (with a similar taste to celery) available in winter months. It contains negligible amounts of **vitamin C**, **potassium** and **iron**. The roots should be heavy with a smooth skin.

PREPARATION: celeriac should be peeled, then grated or steamed and puréed.

USES: puréed or **steamed** celeriac is used as a side vegetable. Grated, raw celeriac can be used in salads or added to casseroles or stir-fries.

celery The crisp, fibrous, white or green stalks of a Eurasian plant. Choose celery with crisp, unblemished stalks and fresh, leafy tops. Store in the refrigerator. Celery consists largely of water, but provides useful amounts of **dietary fibre** and some **vitamin C**, **folic acid** and **trace elements**, although these are much reduced if the celery is cooked.

PREPARATION: break the stalks off the base and trim off the leaves and any very green parts. Celery can be eaten raw, or cooked, chopped or whole. Boil, **steam** or **stir-fry**.

USES: serve crisp celery stalks with a **cheesy** dipping sauce or with a fondue. Add raw, chopped celery to a mixed **bean** salad. Use in soups, casseroles and vegetable bakes.

celery seed The seed of the **celery** plant, which may be used as a **spice**. It has a rather bitter taste and should be used sparingly.

USES: sprinkle onto cooked vegetables or salads.

cèpes A wild French **mushroom** of the boletus family, with a woody flavour.

cereal Any of a number of species of grass (e.g. **wheat**, **oat**, **rice**, **maize**, **rye**, **barley** and **millet**) that has an edible seed. Cereals are staple foods throughout the world. Many cereals can be eaten whole, like rice, and they can all be ground to make **flour**. They are usually eaten in the form of flour, **bread**, **pasta** or breakfast cereals.

Cereals are an important source of **protein** in the **vegetarian** diet, especially when combined with **pulses** or **dairy products**. Wholegrain cereals are also a very good source of complex **carbohydrate**, **dietary fibre**, **calcium**, **iron** and **B complex vitamins**, as well as some **trace elements**. Raw cereals may contain small amounts of **phytic acid**, which can inhibit the absorption of useful vitamins and minerals, but thorough cooking will destroy it.

chanterelle A large, orange, trumpet-shaped wild **mushroom**, usually served stewed. It has a delicate, somewhat nutty flavour. When buying look for plump, spongy ones, avoiding any that have wrinkled, shrivelled caps.

chapati or **chapatti** A flat, coarse, unleavened Indian **bread** made from finely ground whole-wheat **flour**. Chapatis contain **starch** and some **protein** and **dietary fibre**, as well as some **calcium** and **B complex vitamins**. Because the dough is unrisen they may also contain some **phytic acid**.

PREPARATION: ready-made chapatis may be eaten cold or warmed in an oven.

USES: they can be served with Indian-style dishes or with casseroles.

chard See **Swiss chard**.

charentais melon A small, round **melon** with pale green, striped skin and sweet, fragrant, orange flesh.

chayote or **cheyote** (also called **cho cho**, **choko**, **chow chow**, **christophene** or **mirliton**) A type of **squash** with a pear-like shape and green skin. It can be used like a **marrow** but the flesh is less watery and firmer.

PREPARATION: slice and fry in **butter** or halve and bake in a hot oven for around 20 minutes. Alternatively, cut into pieces and boil for 30 minutes.

USES: serve as a side vegetable or add cooled, cooked pieces to a salad. Stuff, like a marrow, with a savoury **nut**- or **cereal**-based mixture.

cheese A **dairy product** made from the curd of **milk** separated from the **whey**. There are an enormous variety of cheeses, but by far the majority are manufactured using **animal rennet** (an enzyme obtained from calves' stomachs) to separate the milk. Cheeses made in this way are not considered truly suitable for **vegetarians**, and some cheeses are available made with **microbial** or **genetically engineered rennet**. However, the choice of true vegetarian cheeses is limited and in practice many vegetarians eat cheeses made with animal rennet.

Cheese is an important source of **protein** in the vegetarian diet. It contains a high proportion of saturated fats (see **polyunsaturated fats**) and can be a fattening food, especially if used as a meat replacement and eaten to excess. Cheese is also high in **calcium**, **vitamin A** and **riboflavin**. Some varieties are high in **salt**. See also **soya cheese**.

cherimoya A large, round variety of **custard apple** with smooth green scales and pale green skin. It has aromatic, creamy flesh with a pineapple-like flavour.

cherry The small, round, red, purple or black **fruit** of the cherry tree. Look for glossy-skinned cherries with their stems still attached. They can be stored in the refrigerator, but are best used soon after purchase.

Cherries are high in **sugars** and also contain some **vitamin A**, **folic acid**, **potassium** and **vitamin C**.

PREPARATION: wash the cherries and remove the stems. They may be eaten raw, but the stones are inedible. Cherries may also be stewed or baked in a pie or tart.

USES: as a fresh fruit in a salad or perhaps with a few drops of liqueur. Use in cooked fruit desserts and to make jam.

cherry tomato   A very small, bite-sized **tomato** with a sweet taste, but sometimes a tough skin.

chervil   The leaves of a small Eurasian shrub that have a pleasant **aniseed** flavour and are used as a **herb**. It is sold fresh and dried.

USES: chervil can be used in salads and soups.

chestnut (also called **sweet chestnut**)   The **nut** of the sweet chestnut tree with a smooth, tough, brown skin and wrinkled-looking, soft, yellowish flesh. Chestnuts can be obtained fresh, canned (in syrup, water or as a purée), dried, or (depending on the season) hot and roasted from street vendors. Chestnuts provide much less **fat** than most other nuts and are therefore less Calorific.

PREPARATION: chestnuts can be baked, boiled or crystallized in **sugar** (marron glacés).

USES: chestnuts can be eaten freshly roasted or cooked, then skinned and chopped and added to a festive nut roast, or puréed and served as a sweet or savoury side dish.

chestnut flour   A tasty, **gluten**-free **flour**, derived from ground **chestnuts**. It is available from some health-food shops or from specialist mail-order outlets.

USES: it can be used on its own or mixed with other flours to make breads, baked goods and pastry.

chèvre   See **goats' cheese**.

chickpea (also called **garbanzo bean**)   The small, whitish, pea-shaped seed of a leguminous Mediterranean or central Asian plant, which is a **pulse**. Chickpeas are available dried or canned in brine. They are a good source of **protein**, as well as of **dietary fibre**. They also contain **potassium**, **calcium**, **magnesium**, **manganese**, **carotene** and **folic acid**.

PREPARATION: chickpeas should be soaked overnight then rinsed, brought to the boil in fresh water and boiled for 10 minutes. They can then be simmered for between one and two hours until tender. Chickpeas can also be sprouted (see **bean sprout**).

USES: cooked chickpeas can be roasted with **soy sauce** or fried with **garlic** to make a snack food. They can be added to salads or to casseroles. Traditionally, they are puréed with **tahini** and garlic to make a Middle Eastern style dip or spread called **hummus**. They can also be ground into a flour known as **gram flour**.

chickpea flour   See **gram flour**.

chicory (also called **Belgian endive**)   The green-white, tightly wrapped leaves of a blue-flowered plant, eaten as a vegetable. It has a rather bitter taste and any leaves with dark green edges are the most bitter. Chicory contains **dietary fibre** and some **folic acid**, **vitamin C** and **iron**, although much of the vitamin content can be lost during cooking. Chicory root is ground and used as a cheap, caffeine-free **coffee substitute** or coffee extender.

PREPARATION: wash and use the leaves whole or chopped in salads. Simmer the heads in salted water for 10–15 minutes and serve, or braise them for 20 minutes in **butter**.

USES: as a side vegetable, perhaps in a sauce or in a fresh-leaf salad. See also **radicchio**.

chilli (also called **hot pepper**) The red, or green and red, tapering pod of a variety of tropical **capsicum**. Chillies are very pungent and are added to spicy foods and bland dishes to add a fiery flavour. Red chillis are hotter than green ones. They can be stored in the refrigerator or dried.

PREPARATION: the seeds can irritate and burn the skin, so avoid touching the inside of the pepper when slicing or dicing, and do not touch your face or eyes before washing your hands well. Alternatively, wear rubber gloves when preparing.

USES: to give spice to Mexican, Chinese and Indian dishes, and also to traditional stews and casseroles. See also **chilli powder**.

chilli powder A hot-tasting **spice** made from dried, ground **chilli** peppers. Store in an airtight container.

USES: add with caution to soups, stews and sauces.

Chinese apple See **ber**.

Chinese broccoli A plant related to **broccoli** with smaller buds and sometimes tiny white flowers. It should be prepared and used in the same way as broccoli.

Chinese cabbage See **Chinese leaf**.

Chinese five spice A combination of five or more dried **spices**. It usually contains **cinnamon**, **clove**, **fennel**, star anise and Sichuan **pepper**, but it may also contain **cardamom**, **nutmeg** and sometimes dried **ginger** root or **orange** peel. To preserve its aroma and freshness it should be stored in a sealed container.

USES: in Chinese cooking. It may also be mixed with **salt** or sea salt and used as a condiment.

Chinese gooseberry See **kiwi fruit**.

Chinese leaf (also called **Chinese cabbage** or **feuille de chene**) A variety of **cabbage** with a tall, tightly packed bud of wrinkled green leaves on crisp white stems. It contains some **dietary fibre**, **vitamin C** and **folic acid**, which are depleted if the leaves are cooked.

PREPARATION: crisp fresh Chinese leaves are commonly washed and used whole or shredded into salads. It may also be stir-fried or boiled.

USES: as a side vegetable or as part of a salad, perhaps to complement a Chinese-style main dish. See also **pak-choi cabbage**.

Chinese pea   See **mangetout**.

Chinese water chestnut   See **water chestnut**.

chives   The thin, tubular leaves of a Eurasian plant, used as a **herb**. Chives have a mild, **onion** flavour. They can be purchased fresh or dried and make a useful kitchen windowsill herb.

PREPARATION: rinse in cold water and chop finely.

USES: chives have a delicate flavour which goes well with soft **cheese** and **egg** dishes. Sprinkle over salads and cooked vegetables.

chloride   A **trace element** involved in maintaining the water balance in the body. Because it is a constituent of sodium chloride, common table **salt**, chloride deficiency is rare.

cho cho   See **chayote**.

choko   See **chayote**.

cholecalciferol (also called **vitamin D₃**) The form of **vitamin D** produced by the action of ultraviolet rays in sunlight on **cholesterol** in the skin.

cholesterol A fatty substance that occurs naturally in all animal tissues. Although cholesterol is essential to the body, the body can manufacture cholesterol from saturated fats (see **polyunsaturated fats**). A high level of cholesterol in the body has been linked with an increased risk of coronary heart disease. It is considered sensible to limit dietary intake of cholesterol and saturated fats. Vegetarian foods that are high in cholesterol include **eggs**, **cheese** and **cream**.

chow chow See **chayote**.

christophene See **chayote**.

chromium A metallic **trace element** necessary for the metabolism of **glucose** and of **fats**. Chromium is found in **molasses**, **rice** bran, **egg** yolk and **brewer's yeast**. Deficiency is rare because chromium is required only in minute quantities.

cider An **alcoholic** drink made from fermented **apple** juice, which is allowed to mature so that a proportion of the **sugars** turn to alcohol. Traditionally, a piece of pork was placed inside each cask, making the cider unsuitable for **vegetarians**.

cider vinegar The mild, pleasantly-flavoured **vinegar** obtained as a by-product of **cider**. Cider vinegar is less acidic than other vinegars.

USES: cider vinegar can be used in salad dressings and Chinese-style marinades. It is also thought to have cleansing qualities and some people use it like a food supplement, diluted in warm water. See also **balsamic vinegar**; **herb vinegar**; **wine vinegar**.

cilantro See **coriander**.

cinnamon The fragrant, yellow-brown bark of a tropical Asian tree ground and used as a **spice**. It is also available as rolled sticks. Cinnamon has a warm, spicy aroma and should be stored in a sealed container.

USES: use pieces of stick in punches and marinades. Use the powder in baked foods, hot drinks, **milk** puddings, fruit puddings and curries.

citron A **citrus fruit** that looks like a large lemon. It is used solely for its thick peel, which is candied.

PREPARATION: strips of peel are simmered in boiling water for a few minutes, then washed in cold water, and this process is repeated several times. The peel is then simmered in a sugar syrup for about three hours, dried and stored in an airtight container.

USES: as a decoration and in cake and biscuit making.

citrus fruit The **fruits** of certain varieties of tropical and subtropical trees and shrubs, characterized by a waxy yellow or orange rind and mildly acidic, juicy flesh in crescent-shaped segments. Citrus fruits have a higher citric acid content than most other fruits, and most of them are good sources of **vitamin C**. See **blood orange**; **citron**; **clementine**; **grapefruit**; **lemon**; **lime**; **limetta**; **mandarin**; **minneola**; **navel orange**; **nectarine**; **orange**; **ortanique**; **pink grapefruit**; **pomelo**; **satsuma**; **Seville orange**; **shaddock**; **sweetie**; **tangelo**; **tangerine**; **temple orange**; **ugli fruit**; **Valencia orange**.

clementine A small, sweet **citrus fruit**, a cross between an **orange** and a **tangerine**, with shiny, orange skin and sweet, juicy flesh with few pips. Fresh clementines are high in **sugars**, **dietary fibre** and **vitamin C**.

PREPARATION: the skin is easy to peel away. It can be used in marmalade or candied, but it must be scrubbed first as some fruits are waxed or sprayed.

USES: eat raw, sliced or in segments. Use as oranges.

cloudberry An amber-coloured, berry-like fruit of a creeping Eurasian plant, which is very similar to a **raspberry** and can be prepared and used in the same way. It is not widely available in the UK.

clove A pungent, immature flower bud of a tropical evergreen tree that is dried and used whole or ground as a **spice**. Cloves should be stored in an airtight container.

USES: cloves are traditionally used with **apples** and in **mincemeat**. Use whole cloves in marinades and mulled punches.

cob nut A variety of **hazelnut**.

cochineal (E120) A red food **colouring** that is derived from a type of beetle, and is therefore considered unsuitable for vegetarians. Cochineal is sometimes used to colour artificial soft drinks and cordials, desserts and ice creams. See also **additive**; **E number**.

cocoa powder A fine, dark brown powder obtained by roasting and grinding husked cocoa beans – the seeds of the cacao tree. Cocoa powder contains **calcium** and **potassium**, and has a high **sodium** content. It also contains **caffeine** and theobromine, a stimulant related to caffeine.

USES: cocoa powder is used to make chocolate cakes, biscuits, drinks and puddings. See also **carob**.

coconut The fruit of the coconut palm, consisting of sweet, white flesh and a liquid known as coconut milk. The flesh may be obtained fresh, dried, or desiccated. Coconut, including coconut oil, is high in saturated fats (see **polyunsaturated fats**). It can also be purchased as a puréed block called **creamed coconut**, and dried coconut milk is also available. Fresh coconut flesh should be kept covered with fresh water in the refrigerator. Creamed coconut should also be stored in the refrigerator and dried coconut should be stored in an airtight container.

PREPARATION: pieces of fresh coconut flesh can be grated.

USES: use fresh grated coconut in breakfast cereals and fruit salads, and dried coconut in cakes and biscuits.

co-enzyme R   See **biotin**.

coffee   The bean-like seeds of the coffee tree and the beverage made from them. Coffee can be purchased as whole roasted beans, ready-ground beans or 'instant' coffee (where the infusion has been made and freeze-dried to form granules or powder). It also contains the stimulant **caffeine**, which some people prefer to avoid. Decaffeinated coffee may not be entirely free of caffeine, but it contains very little. Coffee can be decaffeinated using a chemical-based or a water-based process.

coffee substitutes   Caffeine-free coffee substitutes are available and may be based on **chicory**, roasted **cereals**, acorns or **beans**, or **dandelion** roots. These are often preferred by those who have adopted a **vegetarian** diet for health reasons.

cold-pressed oils   These are **oils** extracted from oil-bearing **seeds** or **nuts** without the use of heat or chemicals.

collard, collards or **collard greens** A large green-leafed member of the **cabbage** family. It does not grow a head, but produces a loose-leaf top on a stem. It is easily confused with **kale**, and indeed it has a similar taste. Collards provide **vitamins A** and **C**, **calcium** and **iron**. They are prepared and used in the same way as cabbages.

colocasi or **cologasi** A large, starchy, bulbous tuber grown and used like a **potato**, mainly in Cyprus.

PREPARATION: peel off the thick skin with a knife and use the point of the knife to split the tuber into pieces. Boil until tender and mash with **butter** and **nutmeg**, or parboil and roast like potato.

USES: as a side vegetable.

colouring Any colouring agent, artificial or natural, added to food either by manufacturers or at home, in order primarily to improve the food's appearance. **Cochineal** is a red food colouring not suitable for **vegetarians** because it is derived from beetles. Some natural food colourings that come from plants include **carotene**, betanin (from beetroot), chlorophyll (the green plant colouring), and spices like **saffron** and **turmeric**. Some vegetarians prefer to avoid processed foods containing synthetic food colourings, either for health reasons or because such colourings may be tested on laboratory animals.

comice pear A large, sweet-tasting variety of **pear** which ranges in colour from greenish- to reddish yellow.

common salt See **salt**.

concentrated fruit juice A thick, brown syrup, often made from **apple** juice, which can be used as a natural sweetening agent.
USES: to sweeten fruit salads and pies, sauces and breakfast cereals.

concentrated soya milk A form of **soya milk** made with a lower water content, which can be used in place of **cream** or diluted and used in place of **milk**.

conchiglie A shell-shaped variety of **pasta**.

condensed milk Cows' **milk** that has been homogenized and undergone treatment to reduce its water content, to make it two-and-a-half times more concentrated than milk. **Sugar** is also added.

continental lentil A large flat **lentil** that may be brown or green-beige; a **pulse**. Continental lentils retain their shape after cooking.
PREPARATION: to speed up the cooking time soak overnight, then rinse thoroughly and bring to the boil in fresh water. Boil for 10 minutes, then

simmer for about 30 minutes until soft. If cooking without pre-soaking the lentils need to be simmered for an extra hour or so.

USES: in Indian dishes and as **burgers**.

copper A **trace element** involved in aiding **iron** absorption and enzyme function. **Vegetarian** sources include **nuts**, **pulses**, wholegrain **cereals**, **brewer's yeast** and **olives**. Deficiency is rare.

coriander The dried ripe seeds or leaves (also called cilantro) of a Eurasian shrub, used as a **herb**. The leaves are very thin and similar to flat-leaved **parsley** in appearance. The seeds are small, beige spheres, which yield their best flavour when ground or crushed.

USES: the leaves may be added to salads or used as a garnish. The seeds are commonly used in Indian and Middle Eastern dishes.

corn See **maize**; **sweetcorn**.

cornflour A fine, starchy **flour** made from **maize** and used to thicken foods. Cornflour is highly processed and provides mainly **starch**.

USES: to thicken sauces, casseroles and soups, and to make custards.

corn meal A yellow, medium to coarse meal made from **maize**.

USES: to make cornbread, tacos (Mexican pancakes), or polenta cakes to serve with a rich tomato or vegetable sauce. See also **polenta**.

corn oil The yellow-coloured vegetable **oil** extracted from **maize** and used for cooking. It is high in **polyunsaturated fats** including a high percentage of linoleic acid and contains **vitamin E**. It is one of the most popular of vegetable oils, suitable for deep and shallow frying and baking.

corn on the cob See **sweetcorn**.

corn salad See **lamb's lettuce**.

cos lettuce (also called **romaine lettuce**) A variety of **lettuce** with an upright appearance and oblong-shaped head. The leaves are crisp with a good flavour.

cottage cheese A mild-tasting, soft, white **cheese** with a loose, lumpy texture. It is valued for its low **fat** content. It may be made with either **animal rennet** or **microbial rennet**.
USES: cottage cheese is often eaten in sandwiches or with green salads, but it may also be enjoyed with fruit.

courgette (also called **zucchini**) A small variety of **marrow**, with thin, shiny, dark green skin and pithy, whitish flesh. Although they have a high water content they also offer some **dietary fibre**, as well as some **potassium, carotene, vitamin C** and **B complex vitamins**. However, these nutrients are readily depleted during cooking. Choose smooth, firm courgettes and store in a cool place.

PREPARATION: courgettes may be eaten raw, or they may be sliced and steamed or fried. They can be cut into pieces and marinated for vegetable kebabs or sliced lengthways, stuffed and baked.

USES: use raw courgettes in salads or cut into crudites and serve with a selection of dips. They may be steamed and served as a side vegetable, perhaps with a sauce, or added to a soup or casserole.

couscous Fine or coarse grains of **millet** or tiny balls of **wheat** semolina. Couscous is high in **starch** and **protein**.

PREPARATION: rinse and allow to soak up some water. Either steam over a bubbling stew, or cover with boiling water and bake for 15 minutes in a medium oven until the water has been absorbed.

USES: serve like rice with spicy vegetable casseroles or use to stuff vegetables. Make a salad of the cooled leftovers.

cowpea See **black-eyed pea**.

cows' milk See **milk**.

crab apple The small, sour **fruit** of the crab apple tree. They are like small green apples with very hard, tart flesh. Because they are high in pectin, a gelling agent, they are used in jam making.

cracked wheat The whole **wheat** grain that has simply been cracked between rollers. It can be used in the same way as the whole wheat grain, but takes less time to cook (around two hours).

cranberry The sour, red berry of a variety of trailing shrub. Cranberries can be purchased fresh, according to the season. When buying look for bright, red, shiny skins. Alternatively, they may be purchased frozen. Cranberries provide **iron** and some **vitamin C** and **folic acid**.

PREPARATION: wash and remove damaged berries and stems. They are usually too sour to eat raw and should be cooked with a little water and sugar and puréed.

USES: cranberries can be used to make a sweet or tart sauce, to be served with desserts and nut loaf respectively.

cream The yellow, fatty part of **milk**, which rises to the top when milk is left to stand. Cream is high in **vitamin A** and it also contains **calcium**, **potassium**, **folic acid** and **biotin**, but it has a much higher proportion of saturated fats (see **polyunsaturated fats**). Single cream contains 18% fat, whipping cream a minimum of 35% fat and double cream a minimum of 48%. Clotted cream is richer still, with 55% fat. **Sour cream** is lower in fat (it has a similar fat content to single cream) and is easier to digest, because it contains a bacterial culture similar to that used to make **yoghurt**. Cream is exceptionally high in **Calories** and should really be used only sparingly.

Most of the cream sold in the UK is fresh, but it may also be bought canned or in aerosols. Whipping cream often contains added **sugar** and ultra-heat-treated and sterilized cream may also have **additives**. All types of fresh cream must be stored covered and kept in the refrigerator.

USES: with fresh fruit and desserts or use single cream in sauces and soups.

cream cheese A smooth, soft cheese made from cream or whole milk. The fat content and nutritional profile depend upon the type of milk used.

USES: to make cheesecakes and other rich desserts, and served with fruit as a dessert.

creamed coconut A yellow-white block of puréed **coconut** flesh. It is used as a flavouring agent in small quantities as it is high in saturated fats (see **polyunsaturated fats**). It should be refrigerated after opening.

PREPARATION: grate into cooking foods.

USES: to add coconut flavour to mild Indian dishes, soups or sauces. It can also be dissolved in water to make a milk substitute.

creamed smetana A smooth, low-fat, soured cream made from skimmed milk and cream. See **smetana**.

crème fraîche A type of **cream** that has been allowed to sour slightly and to acquire a cheesy tang. The **fat** content is variable.

crenshaw melon A winter **melon** shaped rather like a rugby football with yellow skin with green flecks.

crisphead lettuce A variety of **lettuce** with a large head of crisp, curled, green leaves. The iceberg lettuce is an extra crisp, white-headed variety of crisphead.

crushed chilli peppers Dried **chilli** peppers crushed into flakes which are used as a **spice**. A more manageable way of adding heat to a dish than using fresh chilli peppers. Crushed, dried chilli peppers can be sprinkled onto foods, sparingly, after they have been cooked.

cucumber The long, thin fruit of a creeping plant, with thin, smooth or ridged, dark green skin and juicy, translucent, greenish flesh. Cucumber has a very high water content, but it does provide **vitamin C** and **dietary fibre**. Cucumbers should be firm and are best not over large. Store in the refrigerator.

PREPARATION: slice thinly or grate. Cut grooves into the sides of the cucumber to give the slices a decorative shape.

USES: mainly in salads or sandwiches. Can be made into a spicy relish, combined with yoghurt as a cooling dip, or sliced into an ice-cold punch.

cumin or **cummin**   The aromatic seed of a plant resembling fennel with a taste similar to mild caraway, used as a **spice**. Seeds can be purchased whole or ground and should be stored in an airtight container.

USES: commonly used in curries, it may also be used in vegetable, pulse and egg dishes.

curd cheese   A smooth, mild-tasting **cheese** made from **skimmed milk** curds. It may be made using either **animal rennet** or **microbial rennet**, and can be made at home using lemon juice to separate curds and whey.

USES: as for **cottage cheese** or **cream cheese**.

curly endive (also called **frisee**)   A variety of **endive** with attractive curly leaves. It makes a tasty and attractive addition to a green salad.

curly kale (also called **Scotch kale**)   A variety of **kale** with extremely frilled leaf edges, giving an effect similar to parsley.

PREPARATION: choose curly kale with young leaves and discard any yellowed or damaged ones.

Cut out the tough midribs and wash thoroughly.
Add the leaves to an inch of boiling water, then
cover and simmer for around eight minutes.

USES: curly kale may be braised with **onions**,
herbs and **spices** or eaten raw. Finely chopped,
raw leaves can be used in a winter salad, or boiled
and served with butter or a white sauce. It may
also be served as a side vegetable, or added to
soups or stews.

currant A dried, seedless, purple grape. Currants are high in **sugars** and **potassium** with some
dietary fibre, **iron**, **folic acid** and some **carotene**.
Look for currants that have a good dark colour.

USES: in biscuits and cakes. See also **blackcurrant**; **dried fruit**; **redcurrant**; **whitecurrant**.

curry leaf The aromatic leaf of the curry plant,
which is used like a **herb**. It is available fresh or
diried. Fresh leaves are far more aromatic and can
be kept in the refrigerator for up to two weeks.

USES: commonly used whole as a flavouring in
southern Indian dishes.

curry powder A preparation of finely ground,
pungent **spices** used to make spicy dishes, especially curry. The spices vary but usually include **turmeric**, **ginger**, **cumin** and **coriander**. Store in an
airtight container.

USES: in Indian dishes and sometimes in other
soups and casseroles.

custard apple   The large **fruit** of the anona tree,
related to pineapple and breadfruit. Depending
on the variety, custard apples have thick, knobbly
or scaly skins and the flesh is creamy white and
soft. The skin should be slightly soft to the touch.
Store in the refrigerator. Custard apples provide a
moderate amount of **iron**, **niacin** and **vitamin C**.
   PREPARATION: slice in half and eat the flesh with
a spoon. The numerous seeds are inedible and
should be avoided. Alternatively, remove the
seeds and serve the mashed pulp in a bowl.
   USES: purée and serve with yoghurt or in a fruit
tart.

cyanocobalamin   See **vitamin B$_{12}$**.

daikon (also called **Japanese radish**, **mooli** or **white
radish**)   A long, white Japanese **radish**. Daikon
can be used in much the same way as other radishes. In Japan, daikons are made into pickles and
are elaborately carved to decorate the table.

dairy products   A term used to cover all **milk**
products, including **cheese**, **yoghurt** and milk. It
also covers **ewes' milk** and **goats' milk** and their
products. Dairy foods are usually high in saturated fats (see **polyunsaturated fats**).
   In theory dairy products are suitable for **vegetarians**, unless they contain non-vegetarian additives, such as **cochineal** (a **colouring**) or **animal
rennet**. Some people find ewes' and goats' milk

more easy to digest than cows' milk. There are also vegetarians who prefer not to buy ewes' and goats' milk because they believe such products to be exploitative, while others favour these products for being produced on a small free-range basis. **Vegans** do not eat any dairy products.

damson The small **fruit** of a variety of plum tree, with thin, cloudy, blue-black skin and crisp, yellowish flesh. Damsons have a sour taste and are not normally eaten raw. They provide **sugars**, **dietary fibre** and some **potassium**, **carotene** and **vitamin C**. Choose firm, ripe fruit without any blemishes or bruises.

PREPARATION: damsons are best washed, halved, stoned and then stewed with a little **sugar**.

USES: stewed damsons can be served alone with **cream** or custard, or cooked in a pie, made into a sauce to be served with ice cream or a plain cheesecake. Damsons may also be made into jam.

dandelion A common Eurasian plant with deeply notched leaves and yellow flowers. Dandelion leaves are one of the best-known **wild foods**. The leaves do contain some **dietary fibre**, **potassium**, **iron**, **manganese**, **vitamin C**, **carotene** and **folic acid**, but they are eaten in such small quantities that they are not of any dietary significance.

PREPARATION: wash wild dandelion leaves thoroughly and avoid picking from contaminated roadsides.

USES: dandelion leaves can be added to leaf salads and the flowers can be used to make wine. The roasted roots make a **coffee substitute**. See also **edible flowers**.

dasheen See **taro**.

date The long, oval **fruit** of the date palm, with thin, shiny, brown skin, crisp, very sweet flesh and a long, woody stone. Dates are high in **sugars** and also provide **dietary fibre**, **potassium**, **calcium**, **iron**, **magnesium** and **folic acid**. They may be purchased fresh or dried; fresh dates should be smooth-skinned.

PREPARATION: wash well.

USES: fresh dates are expensive and best served uncooked. Dates can be candied or used in chutneys, or puréed and used to sweeten cakes. Alternatively, chop or split the dates, then remove the stones and stuff with a **nut** or **cream cheese** mixture.

deep frying A method of cooking in which food is wholly immersed in hot **fat** or **oil**. Vegetarians do not cook in animal fats such as lard, but use only **vegetable oils**. **Sunflower oil** and pure vegetable oil are both suitable for deep frying. Deep frying adds to the energy value of foods because fat is absorbed while the food is cooking. It involves very high temperatures (180-200°C) and causes losses of **vitamins** that are unstable at high temperatures, e.g. **thiamin**, **pantothenic acid** and **vitamin C**. Vegetarian foods that might be deep fried include Indian bhajis and samosas, potato cakes and sliced vegetables in batter.

dewberry   A variety of berry that looks similar to a **blackberry**, but has a grey, cloudy skin and is smaller with a more delicate flavour.

PREPARATION: hull and rinse in cold water.

USES: because they are unusual, dewberries are best enjoyed fresh and whole. However, they may be stewed, made into pies or jams and they go well with **apples**.

dextrose   See **glucose**.

dhal, **dal** or **dholl**   The Indian name for any type of dried **bean**, **pea** or **lentil**, which is commonly applied to a thick Indian soup made from lentils or **split peas** and flavoured with **chilli**, **garam masala**, **cumin** and **turmeric**. It is eaten as a side dish with curries or mixed with **rice**, or as a dip with Indian breads.

diet   See **fruitarian**; **macrobiotic diet**; **vegan**; **vegetarian**. See also INTRODUCTION, VEGETARIAN NUTRITION.

dietary fibre (also called **non-starch polysaccharides**, **NSP** or **soluble fibre**)   The structural polysaccharides of complex **carbohydrates**, which are not digested or absorbed in any significant amounts in the body. Dietary fibre is made up of substances that provide the rigid structure to all plants, including cellulose, edible gums and pectin.

There is no dietary fibre in meat, fish, poultry, **dairy products** or **eggs**. Consequently **vegetarians** and **vegans** are likely to include a higher proportion of fibre-rich foods in their diets than omnivores. Some dietary fibre, particularly from wholegrain **cereals**, absorbs water as it passes undigested down the digestive tract and adds bulk and moisture to the stools, encouraging regular and comfortable evacuation of the bowels. Fibre in **oats**, fruit and vegetables is believed to help lower raised blood cholesterol levels, and prevent a rapid rise in blood glucose levels after a meal.

The best sources of dietary fibre are wholegrain **cereals** and products made from them including wholegrain breakfast cereals and wholemeal **bread**, **pulses**, **fruit** (particularly **dried fruit**) and **vegetables**.

dill The leaves and seed-like fruits of a Eurasian plant, used fresh or dried as a **herb**. It has a subtle **caraway** flavour and is thought to aid digestion. Store in an airtight container.

USES: dill has a mild taste which goes well with **milk-**, **cheese-** or **egg**-based dishes and sauces. It can be used in pickles and sprinkled onto salads or cooked vegetables.

dried fruit Any kind of **fruit** allowed to mature
and dry or artificially dried. Because they have a
low-water content, dried fruits are, weight for
weight, a richer source of nutrients and minerals
than fresh fruit. However, **vitamin C** and **biotin** are
lost in dried fruit. Dried fruits are usually high in
dietary fibre and **sugars**.

Commonly dried fruits are **prunes**, **raisins**, **currants** and **sultanas**, but **peaches**, **apricots**, **apples**,
bananas and many other varieties of fruit are also
available dried. Sun-dried fruits are usually
darker in colour and have not been treated with
chemicals, such as sulphur dioxide.

PREPARATION: it is possible to rehydrate some
dried fruits, including apricots, by soaking them
overnight in water or fruit juice. Wash dried fruits
in hot water before use as they may have been
sprayed with a mineral oil to improve their
appearance and prevent clumping.

USES: dried fruits make a nutritious, energy-
boosting snack, although their high sugar content
should be remembered. They are traditionally
added to cakes and biscuits, but may also be used in
breakfast cereals, fruit salads and savoury dishes.

dried milk Cows' (see **milk**), **ewes'** and **goats'
milk** are available as a dry powder to be mixed
with water before use. The heat treatment
involved destroys the **thiamin** and **vitamin B_{12}** in
milk, but some dried milks are fortified with
added vitamins.

dried peel   The chopped and dried rind of **citrus fruits** including **lemons** and **oranges**.

USES: see **dried fruit**.

dudi   A relative of the **marrow** that looks like a **cucumber** and is used in African and West Indian dishes.

dulse   A purplish-red **seaweed** with a sweet, tangy flavour. Dulse is sold cleaned and dried in narrow strips. It can be stored for up to four months in an airtight container.

PREPARATION: soak in water for 10 minutes before use to soften; unless it is to be added to a cooking soup. It can be simmered in boiling water for 10 minutes and served as a vegetable.

USES: in soups and stews or as a cooked vegetable alongside **broccoli** and **cabbage**.

durian   A large, oval **fruit** native to Malaysia and Indonesia with brownish and spiky skin. The soft flesh is pleasant to taste, but the smell of the fresh fruit is similar to rotten **eggs** and is definitely an acquired taste. Durian is best purchased in cans, but if buying fresh ones, store them securely wrapped in a plastic bag.

PREPARATION: remove the skin and cut the flesh into chunks. It may be eaten raw or puréed.

USES: in an exotic fruit salad.

durum wheat A variety of **wheat** with a very high **gluten** content. Durum wheat is used to make **semolina** or **pasta**.

dwarf bean See **French bean**.

eat all See **mangetout**.

eddoe See **taro**.

edible flowers A wide variety of flowers can be used in vegetarian cookery. **Courgettes** produce very large, yellow, trumpet-shaped flowers which can be stuffed. **Nasturtiums**, pansies, violets and marigolds can be used in salads. Rose petals can be candied and used as a decoration on cakes. Elderflowers can be dipped in a light batter and deep fried (see **deep frying**). Many flowers, however, are poisonous and so when choosing flowers for consumption it is advisable to consult a book on identifying **wild foods**.

egg The mature ovum of a chicken (or other poultry or game bird) protected by a calcified shell. Eggs are rich in **protein**. They also contain **sodium**, **potassium**, **phosphorus**, poorly-absorbed **iron**, **zinc**, **sulphur**, **retinol**, **vitamin D**, **niacin**, **vitamin E**, **pantothenic acid**, **biotin**, **folic acid** and **vitamin B_{12}**. Eggs are high in **cholesterol** and in saturated fats (see **polyunsaturated fats**). They should be cooked thoroughly before eating to destroy any dangerous microorganisms.

Many **vegetarians**, including many Indian vegetarians, do not eat eggs for either ethical or health reasons. Most vegetarians prefer to purchase **free-range eggs** and the Vegetarian Society does not approve any foods which contain **battery eggs**. Duck, goose and quail eggs are all suitable for vegetarians, but in practice some prefer not to eat them. **Vegans** do not eat eggs at all.

PREPARATION: eggs should be stored in a cool place, and will keep for three weeks in the refrigerator. Eggs can be hard boiled in their shells, then chopped and added to salads, scrambled, made into omelettes and fried or poached.

USES: eggs can be served on their own or used in dishes such as soups, salads and rich desserts.

egg-free mayonnaise A type of commercially-manufactured mayonnaise which contains no **eggs**, and often no **dairy products**.

egg plant See **aubergine**.

egg replacer An **egg**-free powder, usually including **soya flour**, that can be mixed with water and used as a replacement in certain recipes for egg. This is of use to **vegans** and to those on low-**cholesterol** diets.

USES: in cakes and other recipes where egg is normally used as a binding agent, rather than as a feature.

elderberry The small, black berry of the elder tree. Elderberries appear in clusters in late August

82

and September. The elderberry is a delicious and widely available wild food. It is rich in **vitamins A, C** and the **B complex vitamins**.

PREPARATION: wash the clusters of berries thoroughly and then strip the berries from the stems using a fork as you would **redcurrants**.

USES: elderberries can be added to **apples** or **gooseberries** and stewed or baked in a pie or crumble. They can also be used in jam and wine making.

endive The crisp curly leaves of a Eurasian plant related to **chicory**. Endive has a slightly bitter flavour which works well as a contrast to other leaves in a green salad. Its leaves may be frilled or flat. Purchase the heads when they are crisp and store in the refrigerator. Endives are a good source of **carotene, folic acid** and **iron**, and they also provide some **dietary fibre, protein** and **sugars**.

PREPARATION: rinse well and add whole or shredded leaves to salad. Leaves may also be lightly steamed.

USES: as a side vegetable, salad leaf, or garnish. See also **curly endive**.

English bean   See **broad bean**.

English field bean   See **field bean**.

enoki mushroom A variety of **mushroom** native to Japan, which has a long, pale stem and small cap. The flavour is bland but goes well in salads and stir-fries.

E number A classification of a food **additive**. It was adopted by the European Community to provide a simple and concise way of referring to those additives that are on the permitted lists of every EC country. Those additives with only a number and no E are on the permitted lists of some but not all EC countries. Since different batches of the same additive may have different sources it is sometimes difficult to obtain a definitive list of those which are not suitable for **vegetarians**. The following is a list of additives which may be unsuitable for vegetarians, although synthetic versions may also be available: E120, E153, E161g, E252, E270, E322, E325, E326, E327, E422, E430, E431, E432, E433, E434, E435, E436, E470, E471, E472, E473, E474, E475, E476, E477, E478, E796, E481, E482, E483, E491, E492, E493, E494, E495, E542, E570, E572. Additives that do not have the E prefix, which may be unsuitable for vegetarians, include: 631, 635, 640, 904, 920.

enzyme A **protein** that exists in all foods and is made in the body as a catalyst for many of its chemical reactions, such as digestion and metabolism. Each enzyme performs a specific function, e.g. lipase breaks down fat into fatty acids, sucrase breaks down sucrose into glucose and fructose, and trypsin breaks down protein into peptides and amino acids. Enzyme activity can lead to **vitamin** loss and spoilage, especially in foods stored for a long period. However, they are inactivated by heat, for example, **blanching** vegetables prior to freezing them.

escarole An alternative name for **batavian endive**. See **endive**.

evaporated milk A variety of **milk** subjected to heat treatment to reduce the water content. It is twice as concentrated as milk. No sugar is added.

ewes' milk (also called **sheep's milk**) The **milk** of the female sheep. It has a similar nutritional content to cows' milk, but with more **fat**, **protein** and a higher energy value. Ewes' milk is sometimes tolerated by those allergic to the protein in cows' milk. It is used to make a strong fatty French **cheese** called Roquefort. It is suitable for **vegetarians**. Although some may refuse it on ethical grounds, while others prefer it to cows' milk as it is produced on a small, non-intensive scale.

ewes' yoghurt A type of **yoghurt** made from ewes' milk. See also **milk**.

extra virgin olive oil A syrupy greenish **oil** obtained from the first pressing of **olives**. The manufacturing process involves no chemicals. It is considered to be the best quality **olive oil** and is consequently expensive.

falafel   A Middle-Eastern dish consisting of a mixture of cooked and mashed **chickpeas**, **tahini**, **garlic** and fresh **coriander** leaves, shaped into small balls and deep-fried. Falafel can be made at home or purchased chilled from delicatessens. It is traditionally served in **pitta bread** 'pockets', with a dressing of tahini and fresh green salad.

farfalle   A variety of **pasta** pinched in the middle to look like a bow or butterfly.

farm egg   See **barn egg**.

farmhouse cheese   Farmhouse cheeses are so-called because they are made by traditional methods on a small scale. They may or may not be made with **animal rennet**. See **cheese**.

fat   A large, organic compound found in the body as body fat and as a nutrient in food with a high energy value. The body can make fat from **carbohydrate** and **protein**, only requiring essential fatty acids to be supplied in the diet. As fat is a concentrated source of energy, a high fat intake can lead to excessive levels of energy and an increase in body weight, which can lead to obesity. High intakes of fat, particularly saturated fats (see polyunsaturated fats), are associated with increased risk of coronary heart disease and certain types of cancer. A **vegetarian** diet contains few foods which are high in saturated fats. Examples include **butter**, **cream**, **cheese** and **eggs**. Other vegetarian foods which are high in fats include vegetable **oil**, **margarine** and some **nuts**.

Most fatty acids are non-essential, because humans can manufacture all but two of them in the body. The two fatty acids that cannot be manufactured are linolenic acid and linoleic acid, and these are, therefore, known as essential fatty acids, because they have to be supplied in the diet. Both of these fatty acids are readily available from vegetable oils, such as **sunflower oil**, **safflower oil**, **soya oil** and **rapeseed oil**, and it is very unlikely that a deficiency would occur in a properly balanced vegetarian diet.

fava bean   See **broad bean**.

fennel   The feathery leaves, used as a **herb**, and the seeds, used as a **spice** (see **fennel seed**) of a herbaceous plant. Fennel has a mild aniseed flavour.

USES: use the chopped leaves and seeds in salads and soups or sprinkle over cooked vegetables. See also **Florence fennel**.

fennel seed   The dried seed of **fennel**, used as a **spice**. Fennel seeds have a mild aniseed flavour and are said to be helpful to the digestion. Store in an airtight container.

USES: sprinkle over baked foods and cooked vegetables. The seeds can be crushed and steeped in boiling water to make a tea.

fenugreek seed   The small **seed** of a plant of the **bean** family with a bitter-sweet flavour.

USES: the seeds can be sprinkled over cooked dishes. They may be toasted first, under the grill or in a dry frying pan. The seeds can also be soaked and allowed to produce spicy sprouts.

feta cheese   A variety of **cheese** originally made in Greece from **ewes'** or **goats' milk**. It is very moist and crumbly, with a strong salty taste. Feta cheese is always suitable for vegetarians, because it is curdled naturally, without the use of **animal rennet**.

USES: mainly in salads, sandwiches, and sometimes as the base of a stuffing for vegetables, or a filling for a filo pastry pattie.

fettucce   A variety of **pasta** shaped as a wide flat noodle.

fettuccini   A variety of **pasta** shaped like **fettucce** but cut into narrower strips.

feuille de chene   See **Chinese leaf**.

fibre See **dietary fibre**.

field bean (also called **English field bean**) A variety of **broad bean** grown in temperate climates including the UK, which is normally used for animal feed, although it can also be cooked for human consumption. It has a bland, rather earthy taste and a tough, brown skin. Field beans are usually very inexpensive, but availability fluctuates.

PREPARATION: soak overnight, then rinse thoroughly and bring to the boil in fresh water. Boil for 10 minutes and then simmer for between 30 minutes and one hour, until tender. Field beans are best mashed or puréed in a blender to break down the tough skins and to release the flavour.

USES: good in patés, **nut roasts** and **burgers**.

fig The pear-shaped **fruit** of a tropical and subtropical tree, with smooth, fleshy, green or purple skin. Fresh figs are seasonally available, in summer and autumn. When buying, look for figs that are plump and have a smooth skin. Dried figs are more common and canned figs are also available.

Fresh figs are high in **sugars**, with **dietary fibre**, **potassium**, **carotene** and **vitamin C**.

PREPARATION: fresh figs can be served uncooked. Cut off the stalk and cut the fruit in half. Dried figs can be eaten as they come, or rehydrated and used like fresh fruit.

USES: serve fresh figs with **yoghurt** and **honey**, or sliced in fruit salads. Puréed dried figs may be used to sweeten flapjacks or to add to yoghurt.

filbert A flask-shaped **nut** with a firm husk, a variety of **hazelnut**.

finings A variety of substances used in the manufacture of **alcoholic** drinks. They are used to clear the cloudiness of the liquid at the end of the fermentation process. Examples of substances used for this purpose include **gelatine** and **isinglass**, extracted from the air bladder of a tropical fish. The use of such substances may mean that certain alcoholic drinks are unsuitable for vegetarians, although most of the finings remain at the bottom of the brewing vessel and do not appear in the glass.

finocchio See **Florence fennel**.

firm tofu A variety of **tofu** that is heavily pressed during manufacture. Firm tofu retains its shape well and can be sliced or diced.

PREPARATION: firm tofu can be cut into large or small chunks or slices, and added to casseroles or stir-fries, or assembled as kebabs. Firm tofu takes the flavour of marinades well.

USES: use firm tofu in Chinese- and Japanese-style meals as well as in savoury dishes, such as curries, **kebabs**, **stir-fries** or fried with **soya sauce**. See also **marinated tofu**.

flageolet bean A dried **French bean**, harvested while young, with a delicate, pale green skin and a subtle flavour. Store away from direct sunlight.

PREPARATION: soak overnight, then rinse well and bring to the boil in fresh water. Boil hard for 10 minutes to remove any toxins and then simmer for around an hour until soft.

USES: can be served as a hot side vegetable, or used cooled in salads. They make a good hot or chilled soup and also go well with **cheese** and **egg** dishes.

flavouring A substance, either natural or artificial, added to food to give or enhance a particular taste. Although 'beef' flavouring is often derived from **yeast**, other meat flavourings may be unsuitable for vegetarians. Meat flavourings are occasionally used in **soya**-based **meat substitutes**, which are not exclusively aimed at the **vegetarian** market.

flax oil (or **linseed oil**) A vegetable **oil** derived from flax seeds (**linseeds**). Flax oil is high in polyunsaturated fatty acids and **vitamin E**, and is a good sorce of linolenic acid, an essential fatty acid.

Florence fennel (also called **finocchio**) The crisp, fibrous stem of a shrub with a mild **aniseed** taste. Bulbs should be white or pale green and firm. Florence fennel is high in water but it also contains some **dietary fibre, potassium, folic acid** and **vitamin C**. It should be stored in the refrigerator.

PREPARATION: fennel should be sliced or cut into pieces and eaten raw or braised.

USES: fennel can be used in a salad or eaten raw after a meal as it has a refreshing taste and is thought to aid digestion. It can be used with **tomatoes** in Italian-style sauces and other dishes, or served as a hot side vegetable, perhaps in a **cheese** sauce. See also **fennel**.

flour Finely ground **cereals**, especially **wheat**, used in making **bread**, biscuits, **pasta**, cakes, pastry and many other foods. It is an important source of **carbohydrate** in the diet. Nutritional content varies according to the grain used to make it. It can be made from all sorts of grains including **rice**, from **chickpeas** and other **pulses**, and from **potato** and other starchy **root vegetables**. Wholemeal brown wheat flour contains **starch, dietary fibre, protein, potassium, magnesium, phosphorus, iron, zinc**, some **vitamin E** and most of the **B complex** vitamins (particularly **niacin, folic acid** and **biotin**). White flour is highly processed and contains fewer nutrients and less fibre.

Flours made from wheat, **rye, barley** and **oats** contain **gluten**, a mixture of the **proteins** glutenin and gliadin, which allows bread to rise. Some people have an allergy to gluten (known as coeliac disease) and substitute these flours with flours made from rice, pulses or starchy roots, which are all gluten-free.

USES: the different varieties of flour often have traditional recipes associated with them and by using an unusual variety of flour a recipe can be made more authentic. See also **amaranth flour**; **banana flour**; **barley flour**; **buckwheat flour**; **cassava flour**; **chestnut flour**; **gram flour**; **green pea flour**; **lentil flour**; **potato flour**; **rice flour**; **rye flour**; **sago flour**; **sorghum flour**; **soya flour**; **tapioca flour**; **yam flour**.

flowers   See **edible flowers**.

fluoride   A non-metallic essential **trace element** found mostly in the teeth and bones. It is used to build strong teeth which helps to prevent tooth decay, although an excessive intake can cause discoloration and pitting of the enamel. The best sources of fluoride are **tea**, **seaweeds** and, in certain areas, fortified tap water.

folic acid   One of the **B complex vitamins**. It is supplied in the diet but it is also made in the body by intestinal bacteria. Folic acid is involved with the synthesis of amino acids and red blood cells. It is an important nutrient during **pregnancy** and **lactation**. Folic acid is easily destroyed by cooking.

The best **vegetarian** sources are leafy green vegetables, **pulses**, **eggs**, wholegrain **cereals** and their products, **brewer's yeast**, **wheat germ** and wheat **bran**.

food poisoning   An acute illness caused by foods or substances in them, and characterized by gastrointestinal inflammation, vomiting and diarrhoea. Food poisoning may be caused by bacteria (e.g. **listeria**), moulds, chemicals or toxic substances that occur naturally in foods. All foods, but dairy products in particular, must be prepared and stored hygienically to prevent the incidence of listeria and **salmonella**. **Vegetarian** and **vegan** foods can also harbour natural toxins, moulds and chemicals that can cause food poisoning, and they should be cooked and stored properly.

fortified milk   A variety of **milk** that has had **vitamins** and **minerals** added to it, such as calcium-enriched cows' milk and fortified **soya milk**.

free-range egg   Free-range **eggs** are those laid by hens that are not confined in cages or barns, but have a generous degree of liberty to roam. Most **vegetarians** who eat eggs prefer to buy free-range eggs mainly for ethical reasons. The Vegetarian Society permits only free-range eggs in the manufacture of approved foods. See **battery egg**; **barn egg**.

French bean (also called **dwarf bean**)   The slender green pods of a small twining plant. It is used fresh and harvested while the **beans** inside the pods are immature. French beans contain **carotene** and **vitamin C**, and useful amounts of **dietary fibre**. Store in the refrigerator.

USES: ful medames retain their shape and texture well, and are good in burgers and coarse-textured patés.

fungi A group of simple plants that do not synthesize food using sunlight, these include **mushrooms**, toadstools, moulds and **yeasts**. Many species are edible but few are eaten in the UK. The **meat substitute Quorn** is manufactured using a variety of fungus.

...lia melon A variety of **melon** with brownish-...low skin covered in a net-like pattern of beige ...ads. Its flesh is pale yellow and sweet tasting.

...m masala A blend of **spices** used in north ...n cooking, usually added at the end of cook-...commonly contains **cumin** and **coriander** ...cardamom seeds and often ground **cinna-**...cks, whole **cloves**, **peppercorns** and crushed ...es, which are mixed together and dry

...n north Indian cuisine, including curries ...ishes.

...bean See **chickpea**.

See **pea**.

...ulb of a small Asian plant made up ...loves) and with a pungent flavour. It

---

PREPARATION: the pods must be young and fresh. If they are stringy it is better to eat only the beans inside. Wash the pods thoroughly and cut off the ends. Cut into pieces or leave whole and boil or steam for approximately five minutes.

USES: as a hot vegetable or cold with a salad dressing.

French haricot bean See **haricot bean**.

frisee See **curly endive**.

fromage frais (also called **fromage blanc**) A smooth, fluid, white **cheese** made by fermenting **skimmed milk**. It is high in **protein** and sometimes, but not always, low in **fat**. It contains **phosphorus**, **retinol** and **calcium**, and often no **salt**. Store in the refrigerator.

USES: as an alternative to **cream** in cooking and on fresh fruit.

fructose (also called **fruit sugar**) A simple sugar (monosaccharide), which is found in more than just trace amounts in **honey** and some fruits, such as **apples** and **pears**.

fruit The fleshy, ripened ovary of a flowering plant, containing one or more **seeds**. Some fruits, such as **tomatoes** and **marrows**, are treated as **vegetables** in cooking. The nutritional content of fruit varies enormously (see individual entries) but in general fruit provides **sugars**, **dietary fibre** and **vitamins** and **minerals**, most notably **vitamin C** and **carotene**. Fresh and **dried fruits** (raw or cooked) are an important part of the **vegetarian** diet. They can be eaten as a breakfast, a starter, a sweet alternative to a sugary dessert, or as a healthy snack. See **citrus fruit** and individual entries; see also **fruit juice**.

fruitarian A person who eats only **fruits**, **nuts** and **seeds**. This is an extreme type of vegetarianism, involving a belief that it is wrong to kill plants by eating their roots, leaves, buds or stems. Such a diet may cause malnutrition in the long term. See INTRODUCTION, VEGETARIAN NUTRITION.

fruit juice The juice extracted from **fruit**. The nutritional value of fruit juice varies according to the fruit or fruits from which it is extracted. In general it provides **sugars** and some of the nutrients associated with fruit, such as **vitamin C** and **vitamin A**. Some fruit juices may contain added **sugar** and some may contain **additives** such as artificial colourings. Pure fruit juice is an important part of the vegetarian diet as it is a healthy alternative to caffeinated and sugary soft drinks. It may be used in place of **milk** on breakfast cereals and concentrated fruit juice can be used as a **sweetener**.

With the help of a juicer machine, fruit juice can be extracted from a wide variety of fruit at home.

Fruit juices made from **oranges, apples, grapefruits, pineapples, pears, peaches, grapes** and **prunes** are widely available in health-food shops and supermarkets. They may be sold fresh, in bottles or cartons, or concentrated, as a syrup or frozen. 'Longlife' juices can be purchased in cartons.

fruit sugar See **fructose**.

frying A method of cooking in a small of very hot **oil** or **fat**. Vegetarians do animal fats such as lard. Frying adds to value of foods because some of the fat by the food during cooking. It also ca **vitamins** that are unstable at high such as **vitamin C, pantothenic ac** Some vegetarian foods that mig include sliced **potatoes, toma rooms** and vegetarian **burge frying**.

ful medames A small, bean, which is particula where it has given its na sisting of ful medames **cumin**.

PREPARATION: so and boil in fresh any toxic substan for one hour, un

is used fresh or diced and powdered to give flavour to food. Garlic has been used since ancient times to aid digestion and as a mild disinfectant to the digestive system. Garlic in large daily doses (30 g) has been shown to reduce raised blood cholesterol levels, but the mechanism is not yet understood.

PREPARATION: garlic gloves are usually peeled and chopped finely or crushed, then added during cooking. It becomes bitter if allowed to brown. Peeled garlic cloves may be stored in **oil** and the oil used in cooking.

USES: in Italian, French, Spanish and Indian dishes, casseroles and soups. A popular and simple use is in garlic bread, which may be eaten as a snack or starter.

gelatine or gelatin   A thickening agent which is sold as a powder and widely used in a variety of commercially prepared foods, including jellies, confectionery, yoghurts, desserts and biscuits. Gelatine is obtained from slaughterhouse waste, such as animal skins, bones, tendons and ligaments. It is not suitable for vegetarians. However, vegetarian alternatives such as **agar** and gelozone are widely available.

genetically engineered rennet   A form of artificially manufactured **rennet**, approved for use in vegetarian **cheeses** by the Vegetarian Society. See also **animal rennet**; **microbial rennet**.

genmai miso A variety of **miso** made from fermented **soya beans** and brown **rice**.

ghee Clarified **butter**. A clear, yellow liquid is obtained by heating butter so that the **fat** melts, the water is then evaporated and the **milk** solids can be skimmed off. Ghee is traditionally used in Indian cooking. It is high in saturated fats (see **polyunsaturated fats**) and, if made with salted butter, high in **sodium**. It provides small amounts of **vitamins A** and **D**.

gherkin A very small **cucumber** grown for pickling and preserved in **vinegar**. It is used mainly for garnishes and savoury snacks.

PREPARATION: eat whole or in slices.

USES: good with **cheese** sandwiches or a ploughman's lunch, or sliced to garnish a vegetable **burger**.

ginger The spicy, pungent underground stem of an Indian plant, which is used fresh or dried and powdered as a **spice** to give flavour to food. Ginger can be purchased either as root ginger, dried, or stem ginger, preserved in syrup. It is said to have a calming effect on the stomach.

USES: in sweet and savoury foods, including cakes and biscuits, curries and stir-fries, and in hot and cold drinks such as ginger beer.

ginkgo nut   A small, pale-skinned **nut** from Asia with a sweet flavour and gummy texture. It is not widely available in the UK, but it may be found in Chinese food shops.

PREPARATION: shell and use whole or chopped.

USES: as a snack or in some Chinese dishes including soup.

glacé fruit   Any of various crystallized or candied fruits. Glacé cherries are used to garnish some alcoholic drinks. Some glacé fruits may contain **colourings**, such as **cochineal**, which are not suitable for vegetarians.

globe artichoke   The large, thistle-like, flower head of a tall Asian plant. It has large, tough petals that have a pleasant-tasting, fleshy base, and a smooth, fleshy, edible 'heart'. Globe artichokes have a high water content, but they do contain small amounts of **protein**, **potassium** and **calcium**. Store in a plastic bag in the refrigerator for up to one week.

PREPARATION: cut off the stalk and remove the outer layer of scales. Wash thoroughly and then boil whole in salted water for approximately 30-40 minutes.

USES: as a dish in its own right with **butter** or Hollandaise sauce. Can be eaten hot or cold.

glucose (also called **dextrose** or **grape sugar**)   A monosaccharide or simple sugar. Glucose occurs naturally in **honey** and **grapes** and as part of the disaccharide **sucrose** and polysaccharide **starch**. It can be made in the body from **protein** and **fat**, and is manufactured commercially from starch by the action of acid or **enzymes**. During digestion **carbohydrate** is broken down into glucose, which is absorbed into the blood and carried to the liver. It is either used immediately for energy or converted into glycogen or fat and stored.

gluten   A **protein** found in **cereals**, predominantly **wheat** and **rye**, which are made into **flour**. Gluten plays a crucial part in the making of leavened **bread**. When the dough is kneaded the gluten becomes elastic and expands, it can then trap the bubbles of carbon dioxide given off during **yeast** fermentation. These bubbles of gas help the dough to rise and give the bread a light structure. Other cereals, such as **barley**, **maize**, **millet**, **oats** and **rice** either contain no gluten or an insufficient amount to make bread.

   Coeliac disease is caused by an allergy to gluten, and sufferers must follow a strict gluten-free diet. It should be noted that combining these restrictions with a **vegetarian** diet may be difficult. The following flours are gluten free: **amaranth flour; banana flour; buckwheat flour; cassava flour; chestnut flour; gram flour; green pea flour; lentil flour; potato flour; rice flour; sago flour; sorghum flour; tapioca flour; yam flour.**

glutinous rice (also called **sweet rice** or **sticky rice**) A variety of **rice** with round, pearl-like grains, which become sticky and slightly sweet when cooked. It is used by the Japanese to make sushi. Sushi is the name given to a wide variety of bite-sized foods made of rice combined with seaweed, raw fish, omelette strips, tofu, or vegetables. Sushi is not always made with fish, and can sometimes be suitable for vegetarians. The name given to raw fish which frequently features in Japanese cuisine is sashimi.

glycerine A food **additive** used as a humectant (to help retain moisture) or as a carrier for other food additives. Glycerine may be obtained as a by-product of the soap-making industry, in which case it is an animal product unsuitable for vegetarians, or can sometimes be manufactured from petroleum or from the fermentation of sugars.

goats' cheese (also called **chèvre**) The tangy, pungent **cheese** made from **goats' milk**. The nutritional properties of goats' cheese are similar to cheese made from cows' milk (see **milk**). Goats' cheeses provide **protein** and variable amounts of saturated fats (see **polyunsaturated fats**), along with **calcium**, **vitamin A** and **riboflavin**. If made with **salt** they may have a high **sodium** content. Goats' cheese is sometimes tolerated by people who are allergic to the protein in cows' milk. It is available made to **organic** standards.

goats' milk The **milk** of the goat. It has a similar nutritional profile to cows' milk, but is lower in **protein** and lower in **calcium**. Goats' milk is sometimes tolerated by those allergic to the protein in cows' milk. It is often produced on small **organic** farms. Some vegetarians prefer this to cows' milk produced by intensive farming methods, but others view it as an unnecessary extension of the exploitation of animals.

goats' yoghurt A **yoghurt** made from **goats' milk**.

golden syrup A concentrated solution of **sugar**.

gomasio (also called **sesame salt**) A condiment made from one part rock **salt** to around eight parts **sesame seeds**, roasted together and then finely ground. Using gomasio instead of table salt naturally lowers the amount of **sodium** in the diet. It can be purchased in health-food shops or made at home. It does not store well and so should be bought in small quantities only.

Good King Henry (also called **Lincolnshire spinach**, **mercury** or **poor man's asparagus**) An ancient perennial plant which was grown in the UK many years ago as a vegetable, but has now largely fallen into disuse. The new shoots can be harvested between April and June, and the leaves used until the end of August.

PREPARATION: the new shoots can be cooked like **asparagus**, and the leaves like **spinach**.

USES: as a side vegetable, or the leaves may be used in many recipes in place of spinach.

gooseberry The pale green or deep red, many-seeded **fruit** of a small, spiny Eurasian shrub. Look for firm berries and store them in the refrigerator. Most gooseberries are too tart to be enjoyable uncooked. They contain some **dietary fibre** plus **potassium**, **carotene** (more in red varieties) and a good amount of **vitamin C**.

PREPARATION: wash and remove the stalks. Trim both ends and cook with a little water and **sugar**. They can also be made into a purée.

USES: stewed or puréed gooseberries can be used in pies, tarts and with cheesecakes, or mixed with plain **yoghurt**. They have a high **pectin** content which makes them ideal for making jams and preserves.

Gouda A variety of **cheese** made in the Netherlands from full-fat cows' **milk**. It has a mild, buttery flavour and may be made with or without **animal rennet**.

USES: mainly in salads and sandwiches.

grains See **cereals**.

gram flour (also called **besan** or **chickpea flour**) A fine, creamy-coloured, **gluten**-free flour made from roasted and milled *chana dal*, which is a relative of the chickpea and the most popular **legume** in India. Some British chickpea flours are made from unroasted peas and the flavour can be improved by gently roasting in a dry pan.

USES: gram flour is used in a very wide variety of traditional Indian dishes.

granadilla See **passion fruit**.

grape The pale green ('white') or deep red ('black') fruit of the grape vine, which grow in clusters and have thin skins, smooth, juicy flesh and small, bitter, woody seeds. Seedless grapes are also available. Grapes contain **potassium** and some **vitamin C**. They do not store well and should be eaten soon after purchase.

PREPARATION: do not wash grapes until they are to be used. They are usually eaten raw, but can be used in cooked dishes. They should be peeled before cooking by dipping them briefly in boiling water and rolling off the skin.

USES: as a fresh fruit, with or as a garnish to a green salad or **cheese** platter, or as part of a fruit salad. See also **grapeseed oil**.

grapefruit A large, sour-tasting **citrus fruit** with shiny, waxy, yellow or pink skin, juicy flesh in crescent-shaped segments and small, woody pips. Pink grapefruits are sweeter but yield less juice.

Grapefruits provide **vitamin C**, negligible amounts of **dietary fibre** and some **potassium**, and they are also low in Calories. Store in a cool place.

PREPARATION: they are usually eaten raw.

USES: halve and sprinkle with brown **sugar** or combine with a fruit salad or **yoghurt**. Grapefruit pieces can be used as a salad garnish. Grapefruit can also be used to make marmalade.

grape leaves See **vine leaves**.

grapeseed oil A light vegetable **oil** made from crushed grape seeds. It is high in **polyunsaturated fats** and **vitamin E**, and can be used in frying or to make salad dressings.

grape sugar See **glucose**.

gravy Traditionally, the juices from roasting meat, diluted with **stock** and sometimes thickened with **flour** and darkened with gravy browning (caramel). Vegetarians who wish to have gravy to moisten a **nut roast** can use vegetable stock cubes, granules or powders, or puréed **mushrooms**, **tomatoes**, **onions**, etc.

Greek yoghurt A variety of **yoghurt** made from cows' or **ewes' milk**, which has been strained, making it more concentrated and creamier than ordinary yoghurt.

greengage A small, green, **fruit** (a variety of plum) with thin, green skin, sweet, juicy, yellowish flesh and a hard stone. Greengages provide **sugars**, some **dietary fibre** and **potassium**, but very little **vitamin C**. Greengages should be slightly soft and should be used soon after purchase as they do not store well.

PREPARATION: wash before use. Sweet fruits can be sliced, stoned and added to fruit salads. Sharp fruits are best cooked with sugar in a pie or stewed.

USES: greengages can be used like, and with, plums in warm fruit crumbles and pies, in fruit salads or jams.

green lentil See **continental lentil**.

green pea flour A **gluten**-free **flour** made from cooked, ground, green **split peas**. It is available from some health-food shops or by mail-order from specialist outlets.

USES: use to thicken soups and casseroles.

greens (also called **spring greens**) The name given to a variety of leafy green vegetables, including young, immature **cabbages** and **turnip** tops. Greens are inexpensive and nutritious, being high in **dietary fibre**, **calcium**, **iron**, **carotene**, **riboflavin** and **vitamin C** – even after cooking. Availability is seasonal and they were once hailed as the first fresh green vegetables of the year.

PREPARATION: greens can be cooked like **spinach**. Wash the leaves and then place them in a pan and cook with the water that remains on the leaves, along with a little **butter** and seasoning. Alternatively, they may be boiled for around 10 minutes and then sautéed in a little **oil** with **garlic**.

USES: may be used like cabbage or spinach in a variety of recipes including soups, or served as a hot side vegetable.

green split pea Split peas may be green or yellow in colour. See **split pea**.

green tomato An unripe **tomato**. These are often available in abundance towards the end of the growing season when fruits remaining on the plant are unlikely to ripen.

PREPARATION: green tomatoes are unpalatable unless cooked. They should be washed and cooked soon after harvesting.

USES: green tomatoes are most popularly used to make chutney.

grilling A method of cooking by radiant heat, using electricity, gas or charcoal. It is often associated with the cooking of meat, but can also be used to cook vegetarian foods. Grilling causes the outside of the food to reach high temperatures (above 100°C) and may cause some losses of **vitamins** that are unstable at high temperatures, e.g. **thiamin**, **pantothenic acid** and **vitamin C**. Grilling vegetarian **burgers** and sausages can help reduce their **fat** content. Vegetable **kebabs**, consisting of evenly-sized pieces of a variety of vegetables threaded onto metal skewers, can be cooked very successfully under a grill.

grits The name given to broken pieces of grain, most commonly **maize**, called hominy grits. They may be prepared like **wholegrains** but will cook more quickly and may tend to lose their shape.

ground cherry See **strawberry tomato**.

groundnut See **peanut**.

groundnut oil A variety of **oil** extracted from the groundnut or **peanut**. It is a light oil suitable for salad dressings, and it is high in **monounsaturated fats**.

ground rice A white powder with the consistency of **semolina**, made from coarsely milled white **rice**. Like semolina, it is used in baking and in puddings and is frequently a first weaning food for babies, mixed with breast milk or a baby milk formula.

guava The small **fruit** of a tropical American tree, with yellow skin and pulpy, sweet, pink flesh. They provide **sugars**, **dietary fibre** and are a particularly good source of **vitamin C**. They have a strong musky smell which may taint other foods.

PREPARATION: cut in half and eat the flesh with a spoon, or remove the inner pulp and seeds and eat the firmer flesh.

USES: the scooped out flesh can be added to a fruit salad, eaten with **yoghurt** or used in preserves.

halva or **halvah** A Middle-Eastern sweet with a consistency similar to fudge, traditionally made with ground **sesame seeds** and **honey**. However, it is also available made from ground **pistachio nuts** or **almonds**. Like any sweet, it should be eaten in moderation, though it is made from natural ingredients. It is normally sold vacuum-packed.

haricot bean (also called **navy bean** or **pea bean**) The small ripe seed of a variety of **French bean**; a **pulse**. Haricot beans are allowed to dry in the pod before harvesting and have a pale white colour. They are high in **dietary fibre** and **protein**, and also contain **potassium**, **phosphorus**, **iron**, **zinc**, **molybdenum** and **manganese**. They are perhaps the best known of all beans because they are used to make **baked beans**.

PREPARATION: haricot beans should be soaked overnight, rinsed thoroughly and brought to the boil. After boiling for 10 minutes they should be simmered for around an hour and a half until tender. Some may shed their skins. The simmering stage of cooking may be done in a soup instead of in water. Alternatively, the boiled beans may be baked in a low oven in a **tomato** mixture for several hours until tender.

USES: haricot beans are very versatile and may be served in a sauce as a vegetable, baked in a cheese quiche, used cold in a salad, mashed to make **burgers** or added to a hearty soup or stew. See also **flageolet bean**.

hatcho miso A strong-tasting variety of **miso** made from fermented **soya beans**.

Hay diet See the introductory section What is a Vegetarian?

hazelnut (also called **cob nut**) The small, rounded **nut** of the hazel shrub, with a thin, brown, woody shell and a smooth, rounded kernel. Hazelnuts contain **protein**, a good amount of **vitamin E**, many of the **B complex vitamins**, **potassium**, **phosphorus**, **iron**, **zinc** and **manganese**, and they also have a lower **fat** content compared with most other nuts. They can be purchased shelled, whole or chopped, and may also be harvested from the wild during the last weeks of September.

PREPARATION: hazelnuts should be shelled and may then be eaten whole, toasted, chopped or ground.

USES: blanched hazelnut kernels can be puréed with **butter** and perhaps **cocoa** and **honey** to make a spread. Ground hazelnuts can be mixed with water to make a **nut milk** or mixed with **milk** and honey for a nutritious drink. Chopped hazelnuts are a useful ingredient in **nut cutlets** and can also be used in sweet or savoury pastry and combined with **egg** whites to make a delicious meringue.

hazelnut oil A rich, heavy **oil** extracted from **hazelnuts**. Hazelnut oil is high in **polyunsaturated** fatty acids and in **vitamin E**, and can be used to cook fried foods or to make a salad dressing.

herb Any of a variety of aromatic plants, parts of which (usually the leaves) are used fresh or dried, whole or ground to add flavour to food. The availability of fresh herbs is sometimes limited, but many can be successfully grown on a kitchen windowsill or in a small garden. Herbs should be widely used in a **vegetarian** diet because they can enhance and alter the character and taste of many dishes. Certain foods absorb their flavours more readily than others, such as **nut-**, **bean-** and **tofu-**based dishes. Herbs are also frequently used as a garnish.

Dried herbs must be stored carefully in sealed jars out of direct sunlight, as they can easily lose their colour and flavour. See **basil**; **bay**; **chervil**; **chives**; **coriander**; **curry leaf**; **dill**; **fennel**; **lemon balm**; **lemon grass**; **lovage**; **marjoram**; **mint**; **mixed herbs**; **oregano**; **parsley**; **peppermint**; **rosemary**; **sage**; **savory**; **sorrel**; **spearmint**; **tarragon**; **thyme**. See also **herbal tea**.

herbal tea An infusion made from any kind of **herb**, which may or may not have medicinal properties traditionally attached to it. The term is also loosely applied to any kind of infusion, such as a **fruit** or flower infusion, that is not made from the traditional tea plant. There is a wide variety of commercial herb teas, which are available either loose-leaf or in tea bags. The most commonly available are **peppermint**, **camomile** and **rosehip**, along with refreshing fruity-tasting teas. Many vegetarians find herb teas preferable to drinks such as **tea** and **coffee** which contain **caffeine**. The popularity of commercial herb teas is growing, because they offer sweet and spicy tastes without **sugar** or any other **additives**.

herb vinegar A **vinegar** in which one or a variety of **herbs** has been infused in order to give it an unusual flavour. Herb vinegars, such as **tarragon** vinegar, are used in salad dressings and delicate **marinades**. Vegetable **oils** may also have sprigs of herbs added to them to subtly enhance their flavour. See also **balsamic vinegar**; **cider vinegar**; **wine vinegar**.

hiziki (also called **hijiki** or **iziki**) A variety of **seaweed** native to Japan and the Far East, which has small, black, cylindrical leaves. Like all sea vegetables it is especially high in **iodine**, as well as being very rich in **calcium** and in many **trace elements**.
   PREPARATION: hiziki needs to be thoroughly rinsed in two changes of water before soaking for 10 minutes to rehydrate. It can then be simmered for 20 minutes to cook, or sautéed in **oil** with **onions**.

USES: as a hot side vegetable, especially with Japanese dishes. It may also be used in soups and crumbled over salads and cooked vegetables.

homogenized milk Whole **milk** that is treated so that the **cream** does not separate. This is done by forcing the milk through a fine aperture to break down the **fat** globules, which then remain in suspension. The milk is **pasteurized** and has the same amount of fat as normal whole milk.

honey A sweet, sticky paste or liquid made by bees from flower nectar. Honey consists mainly of **sugars** in the form of **fructose** and **glucose**, and contains only negligible amounts of **micronutrients**. It has been used as a sweetener, preservative and food since ancient times. Clear honey will begin to form sugary crystals in time. It can be restored by placing the jar in a pan of hot water. Set honey is made from a mixture of clear honey and crystallized honey.

Some vegetarians believe that honey is a more healthy food than sugar. However, **vegans** do not eat honey or any bee products, because they believe that its production may be harmful or exploitative to bees.

honeydew melon A variety of winter **melon** with an oval shape and thick, ribbed, creamy-yellow skin. The flesh, which is usually pale green, but may sometimes be pink, is sweet but often disappointingly watery.

horned melon (also called **kiwano**)   An unusual **melon** from New Zealand, with a thick, bright orange, spiky skin and sweet, green, pulpy flesh with many edible seeds. The taste is like a combination of **banana**, **lime** and **passion fruit**. They are seasonally available between October and March.

PREPARATION: slice the melon in half and eat the flesh with a spoon or as part of a fruit dessert.

USES: serve the fruit in tall glasses with **yoghurt** or in a sponge flan case. The empty shells can be used to serve fruit salad. Slices of horned melon may also be used as an unusual garnish.

horse bean   See **broad bean**.

horseradish   The pungent, white root of a Eurasian plant. The roots have a high **vitamin C** content, but as they are eaten in such small quantities this makes a negligible contribution to the diet.

PREPARATION: peel and grate the root, which may make your eyes water.

USES: the traditional use for horseradish is to mix it with **vinegar** and **milk** or **cream** to make horseradish sauce, but since this is traditionally served with beef it may not be popular with vegetarians. It can be eaten raw if preferred and added to salads, but it should not be eaten in quantity as it has diuretic properties.

hot pepper   See **chilli**.

hubbard squash A variety of winter **squash**, which may have blue-green or orange rind and orange flesh.

PREPARATION AND USES: see **acorn squash**.

huckleberry See **blueberry**.

hummus, hoummos or **houmous** A thick, yellow paste made from cooked puréed **chickpeas**, mixed with **tahini**, lemon juice and **garlic**. It originated in the Middle East, but is now widely available either chilled or tinned in supermarkets and delicatessens.

USES: it can be used as a dip, with crudites or slices of pitta bread, or as a sandwich filling.

hung yoghurt See **Greek yoghurt**.

Hunza apricot A whole, wild **apricot** sun-dried without the use of chemical preservatives. They are brown in colour and contain their stones. Hunza apricots are rich in **iron**, **carotene**, **potassium** and **dietary fibre**. They form a staple of the diet of the Hunza Indians, a Himalayan race famed for their meatless diet.

PREPARATION: Hunza apricots may be eaten dried or rehydrated in water or **fruit juice**. They may then be stewed and the stones removed.

USES: stewed Hunza apricots make a nutritious, sweet topping for **yoghurt**, a breakfast cereal or a **milk** pudding. They may be cooked in tarts or pies or made into preserves or wine.

hydrolysed protein   A food **additive** used to add flavour to soups, **soya sauce**, processed cheese and packet foods. Hydrolysed proteins may be from either an animal or a plant source. Hydrolysed vegetable protein is obtained from **soya beans**.

iceberg lettuce   See **crisphead lettuce**.

ice cream   A sweet, frozen food traditionally made with **cream**, **egg** yolks and **sugar**, and often flavoured with fruits. Ice cream is now more likely to contain **vegetable fat**, non-fat solids of **milk**, sugar, emulsifiers, stabilizers, flavours and colouring. Except for dairy ice cream, commercial varieties do not contain cream. Vegetarians should be aware that some of the food additives sometimes used in the commercial manufacture of ice creams may be derived from animal sources. It is possible to buy ice creams made from **soya milk**, frozen **yoghurt** or sorbets made with fruit juice. Additive-free ice cream can also be made at home if a freezer is available.

Indian date   See **tamarind**.

Indian fig   See **prickly pear**.

Indian plum   See **ber**.

infant diet   See **baby food**.

insoluble fibre A type of **dietary fibre**, which is not digested by the body and adds bulk and moisture to the stools. See also **soluble fibre**.

iodine An essential **trace element** concentrated in the thyroid gland. It is necessary for the production of the thyroid hormones and involved in metabolism. **Kelp** and other **seaweeds** are rich in iodine but the major dietary sources for **vegetarians** are **milk** and **dairy products**. Those who do not eat dairy foods may wish to supplement their diets with iodine.

Irish moss See **carrageen**.

iron A metallic **trace element**, an important component of haemoglobin (the compound in red blood cells that transports oxygen from the lungs to all parts of the body). A proportion of the body's iron is stored in the liver. Although the best source of iron is meat, it is possible to achieve a balanced vegetarian diet that provides ample iron. Vegetarians who do not eat a balanced and varied diet risk iron deficiency and anaemia. This is more likely to occur in women who suffer heavy menstrual blood loss.

Vegetarian foods that contain iron include wholegrain **cereals**, **nuts**, **seeds** and **pulses**, **dried fruits**, such as **apricots**, **peaches** and **prunes**, and green **vegetables**, such as **spinach**, **cabbage** and **watercress**. The absorption of iron in plant foods is improved if **vitamin C** is consumed at the same meal. Good vegetarian sources of vitamin C include **citrus fruits**, red and green **peppers**, **parsley** and leafy green vegetables.

The absorption of iron by the body is impaired by tannin, an astringent chemical most commonly encountered in tea. It is, therefore, advisable not to drink tea with a meal. A certain amount of iron **leaches** out during cooking into the cooking water, but this can be recovered if the cooking water is used to make a gravy or sauce. Otherwise, iron contents are little-affected by cooking, processing and storage. See also INTRODUCTION, VEGETARIAN NUTRITION.

isinglass A **gelatine** made from the air bladders of freshwater fish, used as a clarifying agent.

iziki See **hiziki**.

jack fruit or **jak fruit** A very large, oval **fruit** with a hard, thick, warty, greenish skin and juicy flesh, which is fragrant and delicious when ripe. Because the skin is so thick, it is difficult to tell when the fruit is ripe, and the unripe flesh is insipid.

PREPARATION: slice the fruit in half and scoop out the flesh, removing the large seeds.

USES: the flesh can be served with **yoghurt** or **cream**, as part of a fruit salad or baked in a pie or tart. The **seeds** may also be roasted and served as a nutritious snack or used as a garnish.

jalapeno pepper A hot, red **chilli** pepper with a distinctive, shortened shape.

Japanese bunching onion See **Welsh onion**.

Japanese medlar See **loquat**.

Japanese radish See **daikon**.

jasmine rice (also called **Thai fragrant rice**) An aromatic **rice** similar to **basmati rice**, but with a slightly milder flavour. Although it is a **long-grain rice** it becomes soft and slightly sticky when cooked. It is an ideal rice to serve with Chinese or Southeast Asian food.

Java plum See **tamarillo**.

jelly Most fruit and savoury jellies are made using **gelatine** and are, therefore, not suitable for vegetarians. However, some ready-made jellies and jelly crystals are made using a vegetarian gelatine substitute.

Jerusalem artichoke The smooth, underground tuber of a North American variety of sunflower, which is cooked and eaten as a root vegetable. Jerusalem artichokes contain **starch**, **dietary fibre** and small amounts of **protein**, and are a rich source of **potassium**. They should be stored in a plastic bag in the refrigerator and will stay fresh for up to two weeks.

PREPARATION: scrub the tubers and then boil in
their skins in water containing a teaspoonful of
vinegar to prevent discolouration. Boil for 20-25
minutes and then peel before serving, or eat them
with their skins if preferred.

USES: Jerusalem artichokes can be roasted or
sliced and fried in the same way as **potatoes**.
Boiled, mashed artichokes can be served as a side
vegetable, made into a soup, or shaped into small
balls and fried.

jicama A round, fat, root vegetable with a crisp
texture. The major nutrient available is **starch**.
Look for firm roots which are not shrivelled or
sprouting, and store in a cool, dry, dark place or
loosely wrapped in a refrigerator for up to one
week.

PREPARATION: peel off the rough brown skin
and cut into pieces, then boil in salted water until
tender. Jicama may also be grated and eaten raw.

USES: raw grated jicama can be used in salads.
The cooked root has a crisp texture similar to
water chestnuts and can be used as a side vegetable.

jujube See **ber**.

juniper berry The small, purple berry of a
northern hemisphere shrub, used dried as a **spice**
to give flavour to foods and in the making of gin.
Store in a sealed container.

USES: juniper berries should not be used excessively during pregnancy as they may cause abortion. However, a few crushed or whole dried berries can be added to pickles, stuffings, sauces and **marinades**.

kaki fruit　See **persimmon**.

kale (also called **borecole**)　A variety of **cabbage** with dark green, crinkled leaves, which have a strong flavour and can be bitter. Kale is valued for its **iron** and **vitamin C** content. It should be stored in a plastic bag, squeezing out as much air as possible first, in a refrigerator for up to three days.

PREPARATION: choose kale with young leaves and discard any yellowed or damaged ones. Cut out the tough midribs and wash thoroughly. Add the leaves to an inch of boiling water, then cover and simmer for around eight minutes.

USES: kale may be braised with **onions**, **herbs** and **spices** or eaten raw. Finely chopped, raw, kale leaves can be used in a winter salad, or boiled and served with butter or a white sauce. It may also be served as a side vegetable, or added to soups or stews. See also **curly kale**.

kalonji　See **black onion seed**.

kandalla　See **taro**.

kanten　See **agar**.

kasha The name given to a type of porridge, originating from Russia, made from roasted **buckwheat**.

kefir A soured cows' **milk** made by fermenting the milk with **yeast** and bacteria (*Lactobacillus bulgaricus*). Kefir has a nutritional value similar to **yoghurt**.

kelp (also called **brown seaweed**) A variety of **seaweed**, commonly found on the British coast, which is popular in the Far East as a garnish for rice or as a seasoning. In the UK, kelp enters the diet mostly in the form of alginates, frequently used in **additives**. It is a rich source of **iodine** and also provides **potassium**, **calcium**, **sulphur**, **magnesium**, **iron**, **zinc**, **manganese** and **copper**. It has a high **sodium** content.

kibbled wheat See **cracked wheat**.

kidney bean The mature seed of several varieties of leguminous plant (**pulses**), particularly the **runner** and **French bean**, with a characteristic kidney shape and dark red skin. Kidney beans provide **protein**, **starch** and **dietary fibre**. They also contain **potassium**, **calcium**, **magnesium**, **phosphorus**, **iron**, **manganese**, **molybdenum**, **folic acid** and some **niacin**.

PREPARATION: kidney beans may contain toxins which can cause stomach upsets. They must be soaked overnight, rinsed well, boiled in fresh water for at least 10 minutes and then simmered for around an hour until soft. It is also a good idea to change the cooking water once or twice during cooking.

USES: cooked kidney beans can be served hot as a side vegetable or cold as part of a colourful salad. They can be used in place of meat in dishes like shepherds pie and combine well with rice in West Indian dishes. They can also be cooked with hot chilli pepper sauce (to make chilli beans) or cooked, mashed and reheated (to make refried beans) and used in a variety of Mexican dishes.

kiwi fruit (also called **Chinese gooseberry**) The oval **fruit** of an Asian climbing plant with thin, brown, furry skin, smooth, bright green flesh and tiny black pips. They provide **sugars**, some **dietary fibre** and are a good source of **vitamin C**. Kiwi fruits are best purchased when they are just soft to the touch.

PREPARATION: peel thinly and slice. The pips are edible.

USES: commonly used as a garnish for cheesecakes, fruit salads and rich desserts, but may also be used in preserves or as a garnish for green salads.

kohlrabi The thickened stem of a variety of **cabbage**, with white flesh and purple or pale green skin, with distinctive slash marks. It has a flavour similar to that of young turnips. Kohlrabi contains some **dietary fibre**, **potassium**, **iron** and a good amount of **vitamin C**. It will stay fresh kept in a plastic bag in the refrigerator for up to two weeks.

PREPARATION: the stems are usually trimmed, scrubbed – not peeled – and boiled whole or sliced for 20–30 minutes. Drain and serve, or mash them first if preferred. Young stems may be grated and eaten raw.

USES: as a hot side vegetable, perhaps in a sauce, or grated into a salad or sliced thinly in a stir-fry.

kombu A variety of **seaweed** that is blackish-brown when fresh and forms grey-brown strips when dried. It is harvested in Japan where it is highly valued and considered suitable for giving as a gift. It may be eaten either raw or cooked and has a sweet flavour. Because it is normally sold dried or vacuum-packed, kombu has a long shelflife. Once opened, it should be stored in a cool place, in an airtight container.

PREPARATION: soak for five minutes to soften before use.

USES: in soups and stocks.

kuichai A peppery variety of **spring onion** available only from specialist Chinese food shops.

kumara A variety of **sweet potato** native to New Zealand.

kumquat or **cumquat**   The small, round, orange-coloured fruit of a Chinese tree – similar to a miniature **orange** – with a sweet skin and tart flesh. It is high in **sugars** and **vitamin C**. Ripe kumquats should be quite soft to the touch. They can be stored in the refrigerator for up to one week.

PREPARATION: kumquats can be eaten whole or halved.

USES: as a fresh-fruit dish, mixed with a fruit salad or, sliced or halved, as a garnish. Whole fruits may be preserved in brandy.

kuzu or **kudzu**   A Japanese thickener made from the root of the kuzu vine. It is mixed with water and made into a thin paste, and used in sauces and to coat food before frying to produce a crisp crust. It is available from Japanese and specialist food shops.

lactation   The period immediately after childbirth during which a woman is able to feed her baby using breast milk. A **vegetarian** diet should not adversely affect the quality of breast milk or the ability to breast feed. See INTRODUCTION, SPECIAL NEEDS, BREAST-FEEDING.

lactic acid   An acid-tasting liquid, which can be obtained from sour **milk**, from the fermentation of plant matter, or manufactured artificially. Where lactic acid is used as an ingredient in manufactured foods it may be unsuitable for **vegans**.

lacto ovo vegetarian A **vegetarian** who includes both **dairy products** and **eggs** in his or her diet.

lactose A complex sugar or disaccharide, found in **milk** and which is sometimes called milk sugar. As an ingredient, lactose is not suitable for **vegans**. The human body manufactures lactose from a combination of two simple sugars, or monosaccharides, glucose and galactose. See **sugars**.

lacto vegetarian A **vegetarian** who includes **dairy products**, but not **eggs**, in his or her diet.

ladies' fingers See **okra**.

lamb's lettuce (also called **corn salad** or **mâche**) A variety of **lettuce** with small, soft, rounded leaves. It has a delicate, nut-like flavour and a chewy rather than crisp texture. Although relatively expensive it is a useful source of greens in the winter months. Choose a lettuce with fresh, blue-green leaves and avoid those that are wilted or dry. Lamb's lettuce does not keep well but may last a day or two in the refrigerator.

PREPARATION: rinse in cold water and trim the bases of the leaves.

USES: best used as an ingredient in a salad, though it may also be steamed and eaten as a vegetable.

landcress (also called **American cress**) A plant closely related to **watercress**, but which is grown on land.

PREPARATION AND USES: see watercress.

lard A solid, white **fat** derived from the body fat of slaughtered pigs. Lard is not suitable for vegetarians, and vegetarians should be aware that lard is sometimes used by commercial manufacturers in biscuits and pastries.

lasagne A variety of **pasta** shaped in broad, flat strips. It is most commonly used in layers with **cheese** and **tomato** sauces to make an Italian dish also called lasagne.

lavan melon A winter **melon** that is similar to, but generally juicier and sweeter than, the **honeydew melon**.

laver A red or green **seaweed** with thin, flat, wide fronds of irregular shape, harvested and eaten worldwide, but especially along the coast of Wales. It has a smell like **cabbage** and tastes like **spinach**. It is a relative of **nori**, a seaweed popular in Japan. Laver is rich in **iodine** and **B complex vitamins** and **vitamin C**.

PREPARATION: laver must be thoroughly washed to remove any sand. It is then boiled in a little water with a few drops of **vinegar** until it is soft, like cooked spinach.

USES: serve as a hot side vegetable, seasoned with **pepper**, or shape into flat cakes, coat with breadcrumbs or **oatmeal** and fry. In South Wales blocks of boiled laver are sold as laver bread. This is traditionally fried in bacon fat to make a Welsh delicacy, which is not suitable for **vegetarians**.

leaching The draining of **vitamins** and **minerals** from foods into the cooking water during cooking, or into the drip during thawing. The vitamins most likely to be lost by leaching are the **B complex vitamins** (especially **niacin, folic acid, thiamin** and **riboflavin**) and **vitamin C**. Losses by leaching can be minimized by using very little cooking water and by reserving the water for use in a stock, soup or sauce.

Some minerals, such as **potassium** and **magnesium**, are also leached into cooking water. Up to 66% of the magnesium can be lost when vegetables are boiled, but it is recovered if the liquid is used for sauce or gravy.

leaf beet See **Swiss chard**.

leaf vegetables The term used to describe vegetables grown primarily for their leaves, such as **cabbages** and **lettuces**.

lecithin A food **additive** used as an **antioxidant** and emulsifier, especially in **margarine** and chocolate. Lecithin may be derived from **battery eggs**, in which case it may not be acceptable to **vegetarians**. However, it is more commonly obtained from **soya beans** as a by-product of oil extraction.

lectins Substances found in most **pulses**, particularly raw or undercooked **kidney beans**, **butter beans** and **runner beans**. Lectins are toxic but they are destroyed by boiling (dried beans must be boiled for at least 10 minutes) or by sprouting. If lectins are ingested, they may cause nausea, vomiting and diarrhoea.

leek A **vegetable** of the lily family, related to the **onion**, with a slender white bulb, cylindrical stem and broad, flat leaves. Leeks contain **sugars**, **dietary fibre** and small amounts of **protein**. They contain **iron** and some **carotene** in the green leaves. They can be stored in a plastic bag in the refrigerator for up to five days.

PREPARATION: a problem with leeks is that as they grow they often trap soil and grit between their layers. The best way to clean them is to halve them lengthways and rinse each leaf individually. Leeks can be boiled for around 10 minutes or braised in stock or butter, or sliced into rings and stir fried.

USES: in leek and potato soup, leek flans, casseroles or raw, sliced into a salad.

legume The fruit of the leguminous family of plants consisting of a pod enclosing seeds, which are eaten as **vegetables**. Legumes include, most notably, **beans**, **peas** and **lentils**, and unlike most vegetables they are a good source of **protein**. Dried legumes are known as **pulses**.

lemon A small, yellow and very acidic **citrus fruit** native to Southeast Asia. They are generally used in cooking for their juice and for their grated rind, which can flavour sweet and savoury dishes. Lemon juice is high in **vitamin C** and the rind contains **pectin**, which is useful in jam making.

PREPARATION: lemons can be halved and squeezed, scrubbed and the rind grated, or cut into slices.

USES: lemons are too tart to be eaten fresh. They can be sliced and used as a colourful garnish and the juice can be sprinkled onto dishes to add flavour. The grated rind can be used in cakes and also in curries, as well as in lemon mousses or cheesecakes.

lemon balm A **herb** with large, crinkly leaves and a strong, **lemon** scent. It is available fresh or dried.

USES: in soups, especially chilled soups, and salads. It can also be used in cool summer drinks and as a refreshing tea.

lemon grass A variety of **herb** which has a strong, lemon scent and long, thin, grey-green leaves. Lemon grass can be chopped into salads or used as a garnish, and is one of the main herbs used in Thai cooking. It is traditionally taken as a **herbal tea**, which is considered to alleviate fevers and relieve the symptons of colds and influenza.

lentil A highly nutritious **pulse** originating from southwest Asia. Red, green and brown lentils all have similar nutritional values. Unlike other pulses, they do not need to be soaked before cooking.

Lentils are rich in **protein**, **starch**, **dietary fibre** and **sugars**. Lentils contain **potassium**, **phosphorus**, **copper**, **sulphur**, **molybdenum**, **thiamin**, **niacin**, **vitamin B₆** and **pantothenic acid**. They contain **iron**, **zinc**, **calcium** and **magnesium**, but also **phytic acid**, which interferes with the absorption of these minerals. More iron is absorbed if lentils are eaten with foods containing **vitamin C**. Many of these nutrients, especially the vitamins, are depleted by boiling, but this can be avoided if the lentils are allowed to absorb all the water by the time they are cooked. Lentils may also be sprouted. **Lectins** present in lentils are broken down by boiling for at least 10 minutes, and phytic acid is broken down by thoroughly rinsing the lentils and soaking them in water. See **brown lentil**; **continental lentil**; **split lentil**; **puy lentil**.

lentil flour A **gluten**-free **flour** made from cooked, ground **lentils**. It is available from some health-food shops or by mail-order from specialist outlets.

USES: as a thickener in soups and casseroles, or in pastry and baked goods.

lettuce The leaves of a variety of leafy green plants. Although lettuce does contain a little **dietary fibre** and **protein**, as well as **carotene**, **vitamin C** and **folic acid**, the quantity eaten means that it makes only a negligible contribution to an overall diet.

PREPARATION: wash each leaf thoroughly in cold water and dry with kitchen paper or in a salad spinner. Lettuce is usually eaten raw either as leaves or shredded as a salad vegetable, but it may also be cooked and eaten like **spinach**.

USES: most commonly in salads and sandwiches, or as a garnish. It may also be served as a hot vegetable or used in a soufflé, quiche or hot or chilled soup.

lima bean See **butter bean**.

lime A small, bright green **citrus fruit** shaped like a **lemon**, with similarly tart flesh and juice. It contains slightly more **sugars** and slightly less **vitamin C** than a lemon.

PREPARATION: limes can be halved and squeezed for their juice, the rinds may be scrubbed and grated.

USES: limes are rarely used in cooking except where their strong flavour is a feature, for example in lime-flavoured cheesecakes, mousses, sorbets, preserves or curries. Slices of lime may be used as a garnish.

limetta (also called **sweet lime**) A variety of **citrus fruit** similar to a rounded **lemon**, but with sweeter juice.

Lincolnshire spinach See **Good King Henry**.

linguini A variety of **pasta** shaped in thin, flat strips like flattened **spaghetti**.

linseeds The small, shiny, golden seeds of the flax plant. They have a distinctive **almond** flavour and are high in **polyunsaturated fats**, including the essential fatty acid, linoenic acid. Linseeds are sold in health-food shops as a natural food supplement. They should be stored in a cool place as they can become rancid quickly. They are also used to make linseed oil (see **flax oil**).

USES: as a food supplement or added to soups, cakes and muesli.

listeria A type of bacteria commonly found in soil, water and the digestive system of animals. It can enter the human body through unwashed vegetables (including salad vegetables), unhygienically prepared cook-chill foods and some soft **cheeses**. **Vegetarians** and **vegans** should be aware that listeria can be harboured in vegetarian and vegan foods.

The presence of listeria in the body does not normally cause any problems as there is an inbuilt resistance, but people with lowered immunity, such as the elderly, babies, pregnant women and the sick, can contract listeriosis.

live yoghurt A variety of **yoghurt** that contains the live acidophilus bacteria, which convert **milk** into yoghurt. Some yoghurts are **pasteurized** and the live bacteria are replaced afterwards. The bacteria are said to be beneficial to the body as they replace bacteria that occur naturally in the body but which have been depleted by antibiotics. However, this has not yet been entirely proved. Live yoghurt is considered suitable for **vegetarians**.

locust bean Another name for the **carob** bean pod.

loganberry The dark red **fruit** of a trailing prickly shrub, a cross between a **raspberry** and a **blackberry**, which is more acid than the blackberry but is less intensely flavoured than the raspberry. Loganberries are high in **vitamin C** and also contain **potassium**, **iron**, **carotene** and **dietary fibre**. They do not keep well and should be stored in the refrigerator.

PREPARATION: hull, rinse gently in cold water, pat dry and serve uncooked or stewed, or cook in a pie or tart.

USES: loganberries go well with raspberries and blackberries, and can be used in place of either in hot or cold fruit desserts.

longan A small, brown, round, Oriental **fruit** related to the **lychee**, but with a less knobbly skin and more translucent flesh. The flavour is less acidic and similar to a **grape**. When buying longans avoid any with shrivelled skins. Store them in a plastic bag in the refrigerator.

PREPARATION: peel away the brown skin, discarding the large stone, and eat raw.

USES: longans can be used in the same way as lychees. They are best served in fresh-fruit salads.

long-grain rice The term used to describe a number of varieties of **rice** that have relatively long, slim grains, which may be brown or white. The grains are firm and retain their shape well.

PREPARATION: long-grain rice should be brought to the boil in salted water and allowed to simmer, covered and undisturbed. 250 g of white (milled) long-grain rice should be cooked in 500 ml of water for 15 minutes on the hob or 40 minutes in a medium oven. 250 g of brown long-grain rice needs more water (625 ml) and a longer cooking time (35 minutes on the hob or an hour and a quarter in the oven).

USES: long-grain rice is commonly served as a side dish with Indian curries, Mexican chillies, and Chinese stir-fries. Cooked rice can be used to stuff vegetables, cold in salads, or incorporated into vegetable **burgers** and roasts.

looseleaf lettuce   A variety of **lettuce** that produces no heart and may be harvested leaf by leaf. The leaves can be green or red and as curled and frilled as **curly endive**.

loquat (also called **Japanese medlar**)   A small, Oriental **fruit**, shaped like an elongated **plum**, with tart, apricot-coloured flesh and several large stones. Loquats are seasonally available in spring and summer, and should be purchased while they are firm and unblemished.
   PREPARATION: the fruit can be served raw, peeled or unpeeled. If unpeeled it must be thoroughly washed. They are also good poached in boiling water (the skin should peel away easily after cooking).
   USES: loquat flesh, raw or cooked, can be served like fresh apricot flesh, with **yoghurt**, in a fruit salad or in a sponge case.

lotus root   The rhizome of the lotus plant, an exotic **root vegetable** with a strange shape likened to that of a string of fat sausages. It should be quite hard although not very heavy as it is hollow. Avoid punctured roots as these are hard to clean. It should be stored in a cool place for up to one week. The flesh is crisp and mildly sweet.

PREPARATION: wash and scrub. Chop away the necks between the bulbs and peel away the thin skin. Slice or chop the flesh into bite-sized pieces. Like other starchy root vegetables the lotus root may be baked, boiled, braised or deep fried. In China the roots are often boiled in soup or candied in slices and served as a snack.

USES: as an unusual side vegetable, perhaps with a selection of Chinese-style dishes.

lovage A European plant whose leaves and stems are used as a **herb** to flavour food. It has a strong, **celery**-like, peppery taste.

PREPARATION: rinse the leaves and stems in cold water and chop coarsely. The stems can be candied.

USES: lovage adds a pleasant flavour to bland soups and is also good in **egg** and **cheese** dishes. The young, reddish leaves can be used in salads.

lychee, **litchi**, **lichee** or **lichi** A small Chinese **fruit**, similar to a **plum**, with dry, uneven pinkish skin and juicy, sweet, white flesh. Fresh lychees contain a reasonable amount of **vitamin C**. Store them in a plastic bag in the refrigerator.

PREPARATION: peel away the tough, knobbly skin and discard the stone. The flesh is best eaten when fresh and uncooked.

USES: in fruit salads.

macadamia nut (also called **Queensland nut**) A small, round **nut** with a very thick shell and a soft, sweet kernel, which looks similar to a hazelnut. They are native to Australia but are grown commercially in Hawaii. Macadamia nuts are high in **fats** and contain negligible amounts of **dietary fibre** and some **B complex vitamins**.

PREPARATION: macadamia nuts are only sold shelled and need little further preparation athough they can be chopped, ground or used to make **nut milk**.

USES: as a snack or in a **nut roast**, or with **muesli**.

macaroni or **maccheroni** A variety of **pasta** shaped in small tubes, which may be straight, bent or ridged. It is traditionally used in **milk** puddings and to make macaroni **cheese**.

mace A **spice** obtained by drying and grinding the fleshy coating of **nutmeg** seeds to an orange-brown powder. It is also available as dried 'blades'. Mace has a delicate nutmeg flavour and should be stored in a sealed container.

USES: in delicately-flavoured soups, **egg** dishes, cakes and biscuits.

mâche See **lamb's lettuce**.

macrobiotic diet See the introductory section What is a Vegetarian?

macronutrient A general term for all substances required in the diet in large quantities, such as carbohydrate, **dietary fibre**, **fat** and **protein**. See **micronutrient**.

magnesium An essential **mineral** that together with **calcium** forms an integral part of bones and teeth. Magnesium is also involved in energy supply, nerve and muscle function and the utilization of calcium and **potassium**. Magnesium is widespread in foods, especially those of vegetable origin, and particularly good sources are **nuts**, wholegrain **cereals**, green vegetables and cocoa powder. Because it is so widespread, deficiency is rare.

maize A **cereal** whose kernels, unlike those of any other grain, are normally used unripe as **sweetcorn** or processed as **oil**, **cornflour** or **corn meal**. The dried kernels of a variety with a particularly hard outer covering are usually used to make popcorn.

malanga A starchy **root vegetable** native to the tropical regions of Africa and Australasia. The malanga is like a moist **sweet potato**. It must be thoroughly boiled before eating because otherwise it is poisonous.

PREPARATION: peel, cut into pieces and boil hard in salted water until tender.

USES: as an alternative to **potatoes** or sweet potatoes.

malt extract A syrup derived from malted **barley** which is used as a flavouring and sweetener. It is high in **sugars** but it does also contain small amounts of nutrients.

USES: in cakes, biscuits and in **breads**, where it can help activate the **yeast**.

maltose A complex sugar or disaccharide found in germinated **barley**, and manufactured by the body from **glucose**. See **sugars**.

mandarin (also called **mandarin orange**) A small orange-like **citrus fruit** with sweet, juicy flesh and a characteristic loose skin. Mandarins contain good amounts of **vitamin C**, with some **dietary fibre** and **carotene**.

PREPARATION: peel and eat in segments, or slice.

USES: in fruit salads or sliced in a caramel sauce, or as a decorative garnish.

manganese A **trace element** that is a component of many **enzyme** systems and is important in reproduction. Manganese is found in **nuts**, wholegrain **cereals**, **pulses**, leafy green **vegetables** and **fruit**; **tea** is a particularly rich source of manganese. Deficiency is unlikely with a balanced vegetarian diet.

mangetout (also called **Chinese pea**, **eat all**, **snow pea** or **sugar pea**) A variety of **pea** harvested while the flat pod is still small and immature, and eaten whole. Mangetout provide small amounts of **dietary fibre**, **carotene** and **vitamin C**.

PREPARATION: mangetout may be trimmed and the more mature pods should be 'stringed'. They can be boiled for three minutes and served hot or cold.

USES: in salads and as a side vegetable, perhaps in a sauce. They can be used as a garnish and are a popular vegetable in *nouvelle cuisine*.

mango The sweet, fragrant **fruit** of the tropical mango tree, with juicy, orange flesh and a thin skin, which may be green, red or yellow. Fresh ripe mangoes are high in **vitamin C** and **carotene**. When buying check that the fruit feels slightly soft.

PREPARATION: mangoes can be eaten whole, like **peaches**. Alternatively, slice into segments towards the large stone. The flesh may also be stewed.

USES: mangoes add juice, colour and flavour to fresh-fruit salads. They can be served with **yoghurt** and are also used in sweet and savoury preserves, including Indian-style mango chutney.

mango powder See **amchoor**.

mangosteen A round **fruit** about the size of an **apple** with a very thick, leathery, brown or purple skin and a prominent, lumpy calyx at the top. Inside are white segments arranged in a ring. The segments have a similar taste and texture to **lychees** and each contains a few seeds.

PREPARATION: split the skin and remove the segments, and either serve the segments whole or as pieces (after removing the seeds).

USES: mainly as an unusual fruit salad ingredient.

manioc See **cassava**.

maple syrup A fragrant syrup extracted from the sap of the sugar maple tree, used as a sweetener. It is high in **sugars** and does not offer significant amounts of nutrients.

USES: as a light syrup to serve with pancakes or to sweeten **yoghurt**, cakes and sweet desserts.

margarine A spread made from vegetable **oils** and sometimes with animal oils. Margarines can be hard or soft and used for spreading like **butter** or for cooking. Although they are 80% **fat**, which is a similar content to butter, the important difference is the type of fat they contain. The type of oil used and the method of manufacture determine the proportions of fatty acids in the finished product. Many margarines contain a high proportion of **polyunsaturated fats**.

Vegetarians buy only margarines that contain no animal fats. The term 'animal fats' almost always refers to solid fats, such as **lard** removed from animals after slaughter. The manufacture of butter does not involve the slaughter of animals, and so brands of margarine that contain butter

may be suitable for vegetarians. However, by law
vitamins A and **D** are added to all margarines, and
in some cases the form in which these are added
may be unsuitable for vegetarians. For example,
some margarines contain added fish oil. There are
a number of commercially available margarines
which meet the highest vegetarian standards.

marinated tofu   A variety of **firm tofu** that is sold
ready marinated, vacuum-packed in a bag of
marinade.

marjoram (also called **sweet marjoram**)   The
leaves of a small Mediterranean plant used fresh
or dried, whole or powdered, as a **herb**. It can be
successfully grown as a kitchen windowsill plant.
Dried marjoram should be stored in a sealed container.
    USES: marjoram goes well with green salads,
tomato dishes, **eggs** and with **nuts**.

marron   The French name for the sweet **chestnut**. *Marrons glacés* is the name given to the
French delicacy of candied chestnuts.

marrow   The large edible **fruit** of a creeping
plant, used as a **vegetable**. Marrows have a high
water content and are therefore low in **calories**.
When buying avoid any that are soft. They should
keep well if stored in the refrigerator.
    PREPARATION: marrows should be peeled and
cored. They can be boiled for 10 minutes in very

little water, but they make a watery, insipid vegetable. Pieces of marrow are better braised or added to a rich simmering casserole. Marrows can also be halved, filled with a nut stuffing and baked for about 45 minutes.

USES: not a very successful side vegetable although it is improved with a creamy **cheese** or rich **tomato** sauce. It is better baked or used in a soup or spicy casserole.

marrow bean See **butter bean**.

marrowfat pea The most commonly available variety of **pea**, which is larger and sweeter than the varieties that may be harvested earlier in the year.

matzo meal A meal made from ground matzo, usually in two textures: fine and medium. Matzo meal is used to make a variety of foods, such as matzo balls (knaidels) and pancakes, it is also used as a thickener in soups and to coat foods to be fried.

mayonnaise See **egg-free mayonnaise**.

meat substitutes Meat has traditionally always been an important part of the Western diet, especially in northern Europe and North America, and new **vegetarians** often find that there is a disconcerting gap on their plates. However, by learning to use a greater range of ingredients, including

pulses, **grains**, **pasta**, **fruits** and **vegetables**, they will be able to make more interesting and balanced dishes.

It is often helpful to find out about cooking methods from other regions, as there are many cuisines that do not rely on meat to the same extent; for example, India, Southeast Asia and the Mediterranean countries. **Cheese** is sometimes used as a meat replacement, but it is important to remember that it is high in **fat**. **Soya** products are a nutritious and **protein**-rich alternative. **Tofu** is regularly used in Chinese and Japanese meals, and in the West we are able to purchase tofu **burgers** as well as burgers made from vegetables and from **textured vegetable protein** (TVP). TVP was designed as a meat substitute that would satisfy meat-eaters, and it aims to mimic meat closely. **Seitan** is a realistic meat substitute made from wheat **gluten**. Another such product is **Quorn** which has a meat-like texture, although some vegetarians will not use it because it contains **battery eggs**. See also **tofulami**.

medlar An old, European **fruit** that is not widely available today, though it may be harvested from the wild. It is about the size of a **crab apple**, with a brown skin and a pronounced calyx underneath.

PREPARATION: unlike any other fruit, medlars are picked in November and allowed to decay, or 'blet' for some weeks. The flesh becomes soft, sweet and brown, and can be scooped out and eaten with a spoon.

USES: today it would be used mainly as a novelty and conversation piece.

melon The large, edible **fruits** of a variety of trailing plants. Most have thick, yellow or green skin, watery but fragrant flesh, and many inedible pips. Melons have a very high water content and are therefore low in **Calories**. They provide negligible amounts of **dietary fibre**, as well as some **sugars**, **potassium**, **sulphur**, **carotene**, **vitamin C** and **folic acid**.

The winter melons, including **honeydew** and **lavan**, have very thick skin and it is difficult to tell when they are ripe. **Charentais**, **ogen** or **cantaloupe melons** should smell fragrant and be slightly soft at the end. A ripe melon can be kept for several days in a plastic bag in the refrigerator.

PREPARATION: melons are commonly served sliced into wedges with the seeds scooped away. The flesh can also be cubed or puréed.

USES: chilled melon wedges can be served at breakfast, as a starter or dessert. Melon flesh can be served in balls, perhaps with a splash of **wine**. Puréed melon can be used to make an attractive, chilled, summer soup.

mercury See **Good King Henry**.

microbial rennet A type of **rennet** considered suitable for use in making vegetarian **cheeses**. It is manufactured using microbial activity and does not involve the slaughter of animals. See also **animal rennet**; **genetically engineered rennet**.

micronutrient A general term for all the **vitamins**, **minerals** and **trace elements** that are needed in the diet in very small quantities. See **macronutrient**.

microwave cooking A method of cooking in which food is heated by the vibration of the individual molecules (particularly water molecules) within the food. The vibration is caused by powerful electromagnetic radiation. Microwave cooking retains at least as much of the **micronutrient** content as conventional cooking. Because no **fat** is added in cooking, it can help in cutting down fat consumption. Reheating food in a microwave cooker should be as good as, or superior to, conventional forms of heating for conserving nutrients. Microwave cooking can produce lightly cooked vegetables very quickly and easily.

milk The nutritious liquid produced and secreted by the mammary glands of female mammals to feed their young. Milk of all types is suitable for **vegetarians**, and a vegetarian who drinks milk and eats **dairy products** is defined as a **lacto vegetarian**. Some vegetarians, and **vegans**, do not drink any type of animal milk but may use **soya milk**, which is free from animal products.

Whole cows' milk contains 3.9 g/100 ml **fat**, semi-skimmed 1.6 g and skimmed 0.1 g, and much of this fat is saturated fat (see **polyunsaturated fats**). Milk is a very good source of **protein** and **calcium**, and also contains **zinc**, **potassium** and **phosphorus**. All milk contains **riboflavin**, **thiamin**, **pyridoxine**, **niacin**, **folic acid**, **vitamin B$_{12}$** and **biotin**. Whole and semi-skimmed milk contain **vitamin A**, but skimmed milk does not.

Some vegetarians prefer to buy **organic milk** from cows that are not confined and which are fed only on organic foodstuffs. Some prefer to buy unpasteurized (see **pasteurization**) milk, which has not been heat treated to kill bacteria and is only available from specially accredited herds. However, unpasteurized milk is not recommended for the elderly or young children because of the associated health risk. Unpasteurized milk and dairy products are associated with an increased risk of food poisoning caused by the presence of bacteria.

USES: milk is used as an ingredient in a great variety of dishes. It can be used in a hot or cold drink. It can be used to make **yoghurt** or soft **cheese**. It may be cooked with a little **flour** to make an adaptable white sauce, or baked with a **grain**, such as **rice** or **millet**, to make a milk pudding. See **buttermilk**; **condensed milk**; **cream**; **crème fraîche**; **dairy products**; **dried milk**; **evaporated milk**; **ewes' milk**; **fortified milk**; **goats' milk**; **homogenized milk**; **kefir**; **lactose**; **nut milk**; **semi-skimmed milk**;

skimmed milk; smetana; sour cream; sterilized
milk; ultra heat treated.

millet A tiny, golden **cereal** native to Africa and
Asia. Millet contains **protein, B complex vitamins**
and more **iron** than any other cereal. It is available
as whole grains, flakes, or ground. It does not contain **gluten** and is therefore not suitable for
making leavened **bread**. Cooked millet has a delicate fluffy texture and nutty taste.

PREPARATION: the grains should be lightly
sautéed in a small amount of **oil**. This cracks them
and allows them to soak up water. They should be
simmered in twice their volume of water for 30
minutes until soft.

USES: as with **rice**, millet can be used as a side
grain, to stuff vegetables, as part of a **burger** mix or
roast, and also in a **milk** pudding. See also
sorghum.

mincemeat A sweet-tasting mixture of **dried
fruits**, dried peel, **fat**, **sugar** and often **alcohol**,
most commonly used at Christmas time to make
mince pies. Mincemeat is traditionally made using
suet, an animal fat that is not suitable for vegetarians. There is a vegetarian mincemeat available,
which contains vegetable fat as a suet substitute,
and some ready-made mince pies are made using
it.

minerals Metallic or non-metallic elements that
are essential to the body and must be pro-

vided by the diet. Their main functions are as components of bones and teeth, regulators of the composition of body fluids and as necessary substances for the correct functioning of many enzymes.

Calcium, **chloride**, **magnesium**, **phosphorus**, **potassium**, **sodium** and **sulphur** are required in amounts greater than 100μg per day. The **trace elements** – **chromium**, cobalt, **copper**, **fluoride**, **iodine**, **iron**, **manganese**, **molybdenum**, **selenium** and **zinc** – are needed in amounts less than 100μg or even less than 1mg per day. For individual functions and vegetarian food sources, see the individual food entries.

mineral water Water that contains dissolved minerals. The variety and concentration of the minerals depends on the source of the water, but by law there can be no more than a total of 2 g/litre of minerals. **Calcium**, **magnesium**, **potassium**, bicarbonate and sulphate are the most common minerals present. Mineral waters may be still or carbonated, either naturally or artificially. Some mineral waters have a naturally high **sodium** content. Mineral waters are not treated with chloride or fluoride, their pH level is not altered and they do not contain toxic lead, which tap water can pick up from old pipes. Some people, for health reasons, feel concerned over the quality of their tap water and prefer to drink bottled mineral water.

minneola A variety of **tangelo** (a cross between a **tangerine** and a **grapefruit**) with dark orange skin, few seeds and a sharp taste.

mint The aromatic leaves of a temperate shrub used fresh or dried as a **herb**. There are a number of different varieties of mint and all have a refreshing, cooling taste.

USES: mint is traditionally mixed with **vinegar** and **sugar** to make mint sauce. Although originally intended to accompany lamb, vegetarians may enjoy this suace with a vegetable bake. Mint can be used in the cooking water of new **potatoes** and **peas**, in a green or a **cereal** salad, or as a garnish for a fruit salad or cheesecake. It can also be mixed with **yoghurt** for a cooling Indian-style dip and can be made into a refreshing hot or cold tea.

mirliton See **chayote**.

miso A thick, brown, salty, Japanese paste derived from the fermentation of **soya beans** with or without **cereals**. It is highly nutritious, containing all the nutrients of the soya bean, but it is high in **sodium**. Miso has a very strong taste and should be added to foods in moderation.

USES: as a flavouring. Dissolve a little paste in water and add to soups, casseroles and sauces. See also **genmai miso; hatcho miso; mugi miso**.

mixed herbs A mixture of dried **herbs** sold together for convenience. The mixture often includes **thyme**, **marjoram**, **sage**, **oregano** and **parsley**.

USES: mixed herbs may be used in many savoury dishes including casseroles and soups.

mixed nuts A mixture of prepared **nuts** chopped into small pieces, which is a cheap way to buy nuts for cooking. The types of nut included depends upon what is readily available.

USES: as a topping for breakfast cereals, in **nut roasts** and **burgers**, sprinkled on fruit and **yoghurt**, and in sweet and savoury crumble toppings.

mixed spice A mixture of ground dried **spices** often including **cinnamon**, **nutmeg**, **ginger**, **cloves**, **caraway seed** and **coriander** seed, which are sold together for convenience. Store in a sealed container for freshness.

USES: in many sweet dishes including cakes, biscuits and **milk** puddings.

molasses A dark, thick and slightly bitter syrup obtained during the refining of cane or beet **sugar**. It is a very rich source of **iron** and **calcium** and it also provides **copper**, **magnesium**, **potassium**, **zinc** and **B complex vitamins**. However, it is not usually eaten in sufficient quantities to make a significant contribution to the diet.

USES: as a sweetener in baking. Used in breadmaking it can help start the **yeast**. It is sometimes taken as a food supplement, either by the spoonful or in water.

molybdenum   A **trace element**, possibly essential for humans, that is a component of several important enzymes. It contributes to the excretion of uric acid from the body, to the utilization of **iron** and to the metabolism of **fats**. Molybdenum acts with **fluoride** in protecting tooth enamel from dental decay. It occurs naturally in most forms of plant life, but concentrations vary according to the soil in which the plants are grown. Good sources are wholegrain **cereals**, **pulses**, leafy green **vegetables** and **wheat germ**.

monkey nut   See **peanut**.

monosodium glutamate (MSG)   A flavour enhancer made from wheat **gluten** and used as a food **additive** in a wide range of savoury foods. It has a high **salt** content and in susceptible people it may provoke an unpleasant reaction if consumed in large amounts. These effects, which include a burning sensation across the back of the neck, tightness in the chest, sweating and headaches, are collectively known as the Chinese restaurant syndrome, because of the wide use of monosodium glutamate in Chinese cooking. It is also considered to have possible links with hyperactivity in children. Many people who are vegetarian for health reasons prefer to avoid monosodium glutamate along with many other food additives. It is not permitted in baby foods.

monounsaturated fats A type of **fat** that, unlike **polyunsaturated fats**, has a neutral effect on blood **cholesterol**. **Olive oil** is a particularly rich source.

mooli See **daikon**.

mozzarella A variety of Italian **cheese** made traditionally from buffalo **milk**, but now mainly from cows' milk. It has a very wet, spongy texture and should be stored covered in fresh water in the refrigerator. Mozzarella is the traditional cheese used to top pizzas. It may be made using **animal** or **microbial rennet** and vegetarian mozzarella is widely available.

muesli A breakfast mixture of **cereals**, **nuts**, **seeds** and **dried fruit**, often presoaked, which may be served with **milk**, **yoghurt**, **soya milk**, **fruit juice** or water and sometimes topped with fresh **fruit**. It may also contain **sugar**, **honey** or **bran**. People who are vegetarian for predominately health reasons may prefer home-made muesli, because many manufactured cereals are high in both sugar and **salt**. In general, mueslis provide **protein**, **dietary fibre**, **calcium**, **iron**, **thiamin**, **riboflavin** and **niacin**.

mugi miso A variety of miso made from fermented **soya beans** and **barley**.

mulberry The raspberry-like **fruit** of a temperate tree, with a sweetish but tart flavour. Mulberries are a seasonal crop and rarely available commercially. They do not store well and should be kept in the refrigerator and handled carefully.

PREPARATION: hull, rinse in cold water and pat dry. They may be eaten raw or puréed, stewed or baked in a pie or tart.

USES: mulberries are a rarity and are best served on their own with **sugar** and **cream** or as part of a mixed berry dessert. They can also be used in preserves and winemaking.

mung bean A small, dark green **pulse**. Mung beans are a good source of **protein** and also provide **starch**, **dietary fibre**, **potassium**, **calcium**, **magnesium**, **iron** and **folic acid** and small amounts of **molybdenum**, **thiamin**, **riboflavin**, **niacin** and **vitamin B6**.

PREPARATION: to cook mung beans, first soak them overnight. Rinse thoroughly and bring to the boil in fresh water. Boil for 10 minutes (this destroys any **lectins**) and then simmer for 30 minutes. Mung beans can also be cooked straight from dried. They should be boiled for 10 minutes and then simmered for about 40 minutes. Mung beans can also be soaked and allowed to grow crisp white **bean sprouts**.

USES: cooked mung beans are interchangeable with **aduki beans** in many dishes. They can also be used together for an interesting colour combination. Mung beans feature in many Indian dishes and take up the flavour of **spices** well. They go well with **rice** and can also be shaped into **burgers** or used in soups and casseroles.

mushroom Any of a variety of edible **fungi** that are available fresh, dried, canned and can also be harvested (with care) from the wild. Mushrooms have a high water content and are therefore low in **Calories**. They are rich in **niacin**, **riboflavin** and **pantothenic acid** and also provide small amounts of **dietary fibre**.

The best mushrooms should be plump and firm. The paler the gills, the fresher the mushroom. They should be stored in a paper bag in the refrigerator and should be eaten within a few days of purchase.

PREPARATION: washing can impair the flavour of mushrooms. They are best wiped with a damp cloth and only peeled if really necessary. The bases of the stalks should be trimmed. Mushrooms can be eaten raw, fried, poached, and very large ones can be stuffed and baked or grilled.

USES: as a hot side vegetable, perhaps with a cooked breakfast. Good baked or fried in **garlic** butter, deep-fried in batter, or chopped into Italian **pasta** sauces or French red wine casseroles. See **button mushroom**; **cèpes**; **chanterelle**; **enoki mushroom**; **oyster mushroom**; **porcini**; **shitake mushroom**; **straw mushroom**.

muskmelon The name given to any of various fragrant **melons** with a netted skin pattern, such as **galia melons**.

mustard A spicy condiment made with the powdered seeds of the mustard plant, which contains a volatile oil that gives mustard its hot taste. It is available as a powder, which can be mixed with water, **wine**, **cider**, **beer** or **vinegar**, or as a ready-made paste. It may or may not contain oil, whole mustard seeds, **salt**, **pepper**, **sugar**, finely chopped **herbs** or other flavourings. See also **mustard seed**.

mustard and cress Young sprouts of a variety of mustard plant and garden cress. These are commonly available in punnets and can also be grown on the kitchen windowsill. The mustard sprouts have a peppery flavour which complements the cress.

PREPARATION: mustard and cress seeds can be sown onto compost or a piece of blotting paper, kept damp and allowed to grow, or alternatively sprouted like **bean sprouts** in a jar. Punnets of seedlings can be stored on the windowsill and snipped as required.

USES: as a garnish and sandwich filling. They are a useful source of green food during the winter months.

mustard seed The small rounded seed of the mustard plant which may be either pale yellow ('white') or rich brown ('black'). It is used as a **spice**, whole, crushed or mixed to a paste. The seeds are also pressed to yield a fragrant **oil**.

USES: mustard seeds are extensively used in the cuisine of Bengal. Mustard paste of varying consistencies is commonly used as a condiment. Seeds can be sprinkled sparingly on salads and used in pickles.

naseberry See **sapodilla**.

nashi See **Asian pear**.

nasturtium Any of various plants with yellow, red or orange, trumpet-shaped flowers and round leaves. Except for the roots, all of this plant may be eaten. The young leaves and stems have a peppery flavour, and may be used in salads or sandwiches. The flowers are a colourful addition to salads, and cut up and minced they can be used to flavour butter, cream cheese or vinegar. Nasturtium seeds and the immature flower buds can be pickled and used in the same way as **capers**. See also **edible flowers**.

navel orange A variety of **orange** with a characteristic dimple and an extra segment at one end.

navy bean See **haricot bean**.

nectarine A soft, juicy, smooth-skinned **fruit**, which is a variety of **peach**. When the fruit is ripe the skin should be red, orange or yellow with no trace of green. Their nutritional content is similar to that of peaches and includes **sugars**, some **dietary fibre** and **carotene**.

PREPARATION: nectarines can be eaten raw, washed and unpeeled or peeled and sliced, chopped, puréed or stewed.

USES: in a fresh-fruit salad or cooked in a hot fruit pudding. Also used in jams and pickles.

nettle A tall, leafy plant, generally regarded as a weed, with characteristic stinging hairs on its stem and leaves. Nettles are a useful **wild food** because, as with all dark green, leafy vegetables, they are a good source of **folic acid**, **riboflavin**, **carotene** and **vitamin C**, though boiling will reduce the content of all but carotene.

PREPARATION: nettles must be gathered with care, but they lose their sting a few hours after they are cut or when they are cooked. Young tender nettle tops are preferable and polluted roadside plants should be avoided. The nettles should be washed thoroughly in cold water and then chopped and cooked (like **spinach**) in a little water until soft.

USES: serve as a side vegetable with a little **butter** and seasoning. Nettles may be used in place of spinach in some recipes and they are particularly good in soups. They are also used to make **wine**.

niacin (also called **niacinamide**, **nicotinamide** or **nicotinic acid**) A **B complex vitamin** involved in the metabolic reactions of the body, particularly in the release of energy within the cells. Niacin can be synthesized by the body from the essential amino acid tryptophan if the diet contains sufficient tryptophan, **vitamin B₆**, **B₁** and **B₂**.

Good **vegetarian** sources of niacin include **yeast extract**, **brewer's yeast**, **nuts** and **pulses**. The niacin in certain wholemeal **cereals**, especially **maize**, is in a bound form, which is not available unless treated with alkalis, such as the soda in soda bread. Niacin is added by law to white **bread** in the UK. Considerable amounts of niacin may be lost due to **leaching** into cooking water. However, niacin deficiency is extremely rare.

nicotinamide   See **niacin**.

nicotinic acid   See **niacin**.

nigella   See **black onion seed**.

non-starch polysaccharide   See **dietary fibre**.

noodle   A variety of **pasta** shaped in a ribbon-like strip, often made with **egg**, and used in Chinese and Thai dishes.

nori   A variety of **seaweed**, related to **laver**, that is intensively farmed in Japan and sold dried, in sheets.
  PREPARATION: to rehydrate nori, rinse in cold water and then boil for 15 minutes. It can be used hot or cold. Dried nori can be crumbled.

USES: rehydrated nori can be used like a side vegetable or in a salad. It is good for wrapping **rice** into small parcels and for lining small mould tins. Dried nori can be crumbled onto salads, hot dishes or into simmering casseroles and soups.

NSP   See **dietary fibre**.

nut butter   A spreadable paste made from blended **nuts**, **oil**, **salt** and water. **Peanut** butter is the best-known nut butter, but nut butters can also be made with **cashews**, **hazelnuts** and **almonds**.

nut cheese   A **vegan** alternative to **cheese** made commercially using **nuts**. Vegan hard cheeses are still difficult to find but soft cheeses have been developed using nuts and **soya beans**.

nut cutlet   A kind of **burger** made from a savoury **nut** mixture, which is usually fried, grilled or baked.

nutmeg   The hard, aromatic seed of an evergreen tree, which is finely grated and used as a **spice**. It is available whole or ready ground. Nutmeg is best purchased whole and grated as required because ready-ground nutmeg quickly deteriorates unless stored in an airtight container.

USES: in both sweet and savoury dishes. Particularly good in **milk** puddings, with baked **apples**, and in biscuits and cakes.

nut milk   A creamy liquid made by blending **nuts**, water and **honey**, or, if **vegan**, an alternative sweetening agent. Nut milk, or nut cream, is particularly good made with **almonds** or **cashews** and can be served with a **tofu** cheesecake, fresh fruit or used as the base of a sauce.

nut roast A savoury mixture of chopped and ground **nuts**, fried vegetables, including **onions** and sometimes **garlic**, **celery**, **peppers** and **mushrooms**, flavourings, such as **tomato** purée or **soya sauce**, and sometimes **flour** or an **egg** to bind, which is baked in a loaf tin and served in slices.

nuts The edible kernels of various hard, woody fruits. Nuts are rich sources of **fat**, **protein**, **B complex vitamins**, **vitamin E** and **dietary fibre**, and they have high energy values. They contain **calcium**, **zinc**, **magnesium** and **iron**, but also **phytic acid**, which makes most of these minerals unavailable to the body. Nuts are also rich in **potassium**, which is well absorbed and, unless **salt** is added during roasting, they are low in **sodium**.

Nuts are generally eaten as a snack food, but they form an important part of the **vegetarian** diet and nut-based savoury bakes and **burgers** can form the foundation of a protein-rich meal.

PREPARATION: nuts may be purchased in many forms but whole nuts stay fresh longer than prepared nuts. Once shelled, the brown fibrous skin on the nuts can be removed by **blanching** in a bowl of boiling water or, for **hazelnuts**, baking in the oven or toasting under the grill for five minutes.

Nuts can be toasted under the grill, roasted in a heavy pan with a little **groundnut oil** or baked in the oven. For the latter method, spread them on a baking tray sprinkled with a little oil and bake in a moderate oven for 10 minutes, turning two or three times so that they brown evenly. Nuts can be ground at home in a coffee grinder or liquidizer, and can be finely chopped or grated in a food processor.

USES: nuts can be used as a snack, as part of a substantial main course savoury (see **nut cutlet** and **nut roast**), or in a dessert. They may also be used in a breakfast cereal or as a garnish. See **almond**; **baby coconut**; **brazil nut**; **cashew nut**; **chestnut**; **coconut**; **ginkgo nut**; **hazelnut**; **macadamia nut**; **marron**; **mixed nuts**; **peanut**; **pecan nut**; **pine kernel**; **pistachio nut**; **walnut**; **water chestnut**.

oatmeal   Finely or coarsely ground **oats**.

oats   A **cereal**. Oats are usually purchased rolled and flattened into flakes or ground into **oatmeal**. Oats have a higher **fat** content than other cereals and consequently oatmeal easily becomes rancid and is best stored in the refrigerator. Oats also contain **protein** and **B complex vitamins**. They have been found to help lower raised blood cholesterol levels; this ability has been attributed to the presence of soluble **dietary fibre**.

PREPARATION: oats are not usually available whole although they can be cooked whole in boil-

ing water. Rolled oats need no further preparation although they may be soaked overnight in
milk, water or **fruit juice** to soften them before use.

USES: oats are most commonly used in breakfast
muesli mixtures and porridge, but they also make
a chewy sweet or savoury crumble topping and
may be used in biscuits and **breads**.

ogen melon   A small, round variety of **melon**
with thin, yellow skin, distinctive green stripes and
pale green or creamy-coloured, sweet, juicy flesh.

oil   Liquid, edible **fats**. All liquid fats are derived
from plant sources – vegetables, nuts and seeds –
and so are suitable for vegetarians. Solid fats, such
as **lard** and **suet**, on the other hand, are unsuitable,
because they are both derived from animal
sources. All oils contain saturated, **monounsaturated** and **polyunsaturated** fatty acids in varying
proportions. With the exception of **palm oil**, coconut oil (see **coconut**) and **olive oil**, all vegetable oils
are high in polyunsaturated fatty acids, which are
thought to help reduce raised blood cholesterol
levels, and therefore decrease the risk of coronary
heart disease. Vegetable oils are also a good source
of **vitamin E**, and they are most commonly used as
salad dressings or when frying, stir-frying and
deep-frying. See **cold-pressed oil**; **corn oil**; **extra
virgin olive oil**; **grapeseed oil**; **groundnut oil**; **peanut
oil**; **rapeseed oil**; **safflower oil**; **sesame oil**; **soya oil**;
sunflower oil; **walnut oil**.

okara (also called **soya fibre**) A fibrous pulp of **soya beans** which is a by-product of **tofu** or **soya milk** production. Soya beans are soaked, puréed, cooked in boiling water and strained through muslin. The liquid is soya milk and the residue is okara, a nutritious product high in **dietary fibre**, which can be used in **burgers** and bakes. It is not generally commercially available as a raw product although it is sold already made up into burgers.

okra (also called **ladies' fingers**) The long, tapering, green seed pod of a tropical African and Asian plant, with fleshy skin and many seeds in a thick, gluey sap. Okra contains some **sugars**, **dietary fibre**, a small amount of **protein**, as well as some **iron**, **carotene**, **vitamin C** and **folic acid**.

When buying look for pods that are between two and four inches long, crisp not shrivelled and bright green. They should snap cleanly in half and not bend. Okra should be stored in the refrigerator.

PREPARATION: trim the tops and tails and steam until tender or boil in salted water for 20 minutes. Alternatively, **parboil** for eight minutes, pat dry and deep fry with or without batter until tender.

USES: as a cooked side vegetable or in curries, casseroles and soups. Okra becomes gelatinous as it cooks and can thicken a dish. It is extensively used in American Creole cuisine, where it is known as gumbo (not to be confused with fish and meat stews of the same name).

olive The oily, green or black **fruit** of a Mediterranean tree. Olives are an unusual fruit in that they contain no **sugars**, but have a high **fat** content (mainly **monounsaturated**) and are therefore high in Calories. They provide small amounts of **iron**, **copper** and **carotene**, with more carotene in green than in black olives. They contain virtually no **vitamin C** or **B complex vitamins**. Olives preserved in brine have a high **sodium** content.

PREPARATION: olives do not need to be cooked and are usually served whole or halved. They may be puréed to make a paté.

USES: as a garnish, cocktail nibble, with **pasta**, on pizzas or in salads.

olive oil A thick, greenish **oil** extracted from **olives**. Olive oil is high in **monounsaturated fats** and is a good source of the essential fatty acid linoleic acid.

USES: it has a distinctive taste and is used in salad dressings, **marinades** and in Mediterranean-style **tomato** and **aubergine** dishes. See also **extra virgin olive oil**.

onion A pungent bulb used for flavouring and as a vegetable. Some strict **vegetarians**, such as Hindu Brahmins and Jains, do not eat onion because the flavour is so strong; any kind of stimulation, which includes strong flavours, is forbidden by their religious beliefs.

PREPARATION: onions are not normally eaten as a side vegetable although they can be peeled, parboiled and roasted like **potatoes** and can also be stuffed with a **rice** or **nut** mixture and baked. Onion rings can be fried or deep fried in batter.

USES: onions are a familiar ingredient of all kinds of savoury dishes, including soups, casseroles, curries, **burgers** and bakes, **quiches** and so on. They can also be eaten raw in salads and used as a garnish. See **button onion**; **chives**; **leek**; **shallot**; **Spanish onion**; **spring onion**; **Welsh onion**.

onion seed See **black onion seed**.

orange A **citrus fruit** with three main varieties, the sweet Valencia, the thick-skinned navel and the bitter Seville. Oranges provide **sugars**, **dietary fibre**, **vitamin C** and **folic acid**.

When buying look for oranges with tight, blemish-free skins and a distinctive orange aroma. They will keep for about a week in a cool place.

PREPARATION: peel the fruit and break into segments, or slice across the centre for a decorative pattern. They can also be squeezed for their juice.

USES: eat fresh as they come or in pieces in a fruit salad. Slices of orange can be served in a caramel sauce or used as a garnish. Seville oranges are used to make marmalade. See also **blood orange**; **mandarin**.

oregano The pungent leaves of a Mediterranean variety of **marjoram**, which are used fresh or dried, chopped or powdered, as a **herb**. Oregano should be stored in an airtight container as it quickly loses its aroma.

USES: oregano is one of the most important herbs in Italian cookery and where it is used in **tomato**-based dishes. It also goes well with **cheese** and **eggs**, and can be used in omelettes and stews.

organic foods Foods grown under the principles of organic farming, without the use of chemical fertilizers or pesticides. Only fertilizers derived from animals and plants are used. Manufactured foods made using organic ingredients are prepared using the minimum of processing and without the use of food **additives**.

Many **vegetarians** prefer to eat foods that have been grown organically wherever possible. However, organic farming makes use of animal by-products such as dried blood and bonemeal, which may be offensive to some vegetarians. Veganic gardening is a form of organic gardening which involves no animal products, but commercial veganic farming is a rarity.

Organic products can normally be identified by a symbol on their packaging. The Soil Association symbol indicates that produce is wholly organic, and is widely accepted as the standard to which organic farmers aspire. The Soil Association is operated as a charity and can offer further information on the principles of organic farming.

The Farm Verified Organic symbol is an internationally recognized sign in operation in the UK, Europe and the US, which is also used to indicate wholly organic produce.

The Guild of Conservation Food Producers has a symbol to indicate 'conservation grade' foods that have been produced with limited use of chemicals. Such foods are lower in residues than most intensively-produced foods, but are not necessarily, strictly organically produced.

The Biodynamic Agricultural Association uses a symbol incorporating the word Demeter. The association encourages an alternative view of agriculture, based on a notion of the world as a living organism. Biodynamic farmers farm according to organic principles, and also aim for self-sufficiency. Animals are treated for illness with alternative, homoeopathic medicines.

organic milk The **milk** of cows, goats or ewes which have been fed only feedstuffs that have been grown according to organic principles (see **organic foods**). Animals fed in this way are also frequently given more freedom to roam than intensively farmed animals. Many vegetarians prefer to use organic milk, as well as organic **cheese** and **yoghurt** whenever possible.

ortanique A **citrus fruit** with a slightly flattened shape, which is a cross between a **tangerine** and an **orange**.

oyster mushroom (also called **pleurotte**) A variety of **mushroom** with a large, soft, grey cap. The texture is very firm and 'meaty'.

oyster plant See **salsify**.

oxalic acid A naturally occurring acid that combines with **calcium** and **magnesium** during digestion, and prevents these minerals being absorbed. The most concentrated sources are **tea**, chocolate and other cocoa products. It is also found in **spinach**, **rhubarb** and **beetroot**, and smaller quantities are found in **beans** and **cereals**.

pak-choi cabbage A Chinese **vegetable** related to **Chinese leaf**, with large, green leaves and thick, white stalks. Pak-choi contains **calcium**, **iron** and **vitamin C**. When buying, look for fresh leaves that are curled and crisp. It can be stored in the refrigerator for several days.

PREPARATION: pak-choi should always be cooked before eating. Wash the leaves thoroughly, then shred and cook in a little water for five to ten minutes. The white stems can be **steamed** until tender, or chopped into even-sized pieces and **stir-fried**.

USES: as a hot side vegetable, or in casseroles, soups and stir-fries.

palm oil An orange-coloured **oil** with a distinctive flavour, extracted from the fruit of the Afri-

172

can palm tree. The fruit is made up of a skin surrounding a fibrous pulp within which is the seed. The oil from the pulp is orange and that from the kernel is pale yellow. Palm oil is virtually 100% **fat** and is one of only two vegetable oils that contain saturated fat (see **polyunsaturated fats**) the other being **coconut** oil. It is a good source of **vitamin E**, and palm oil made from pulp is rich in **carotene**.

paneer   An Indian variety of **cheese** with a bland flavour. Although rarely available commercially it is simple to prepare at home. It is made by curdling **milk** with **lemon juice** or **cider vinegar** and straining and pressing the curds. The paneer can then be cut into small cubes and used in savoury curries, in a similar way to **firm tofu**. Paneer must be stored covered in water in a refrigerator and will keep for four days. It is an important source of **protein** for **vegetarians** in India and is increasingly used in vegetarian dishes in Indian restaurants.

pantothenic acid (also called **vitamin B₅**)   A **B complex vitamin** that is part of co-enzyme A, a substance involved in several metabolic functions, including energy production. Pantothenic acid is present in all food except for **fats**, **oils** and **sugar**. The richest vegetarian sources are wheat **bran** and **wheat germ**, **brewer's yeast**, **nuts** and **pulses**. Deficiency is unknown except as part of a severe, general nutritional deficiency.

papaya (also called **paw paw**) A large, pear-shaped tropical **fruit** with smooth, yellow skin, fragrant, orange flesh and shiny, black pips. Papayas provide **sugars**, a small amount of **dietary fibre** and are a good source of **carotene and vitamin C**.

Papayas contain an enzyme, papain, that breaks down protein and so the juice is sometimes used to tenderize meat. Some people, however, are allergic to this juice.

PREPARATION: prepare as you would a **melon**; halve, slice into segments and scoop out the seeds.

USES: serve like fresh melon as a dessert or at breakfast, or serve cubes of papaya flesh in a fruit salad.

paprika A red powder made from ground Hungarian red **peppers** with a mildly sweet taste and used as a **spice**.

USES: it goes well with **egg** and **cheese** dishes, where it can be used to add colour. Also traditionally used in Hungarian cuisine.

parboiling A method of tenderizing foods by boiling them for a short time. Some vegetables, such as **French beans** and **mangetout**, may be parboiled and then chilled and used in salads. Others, such as **potatoes**, may be parboiled to soften them in order to speed the process of roasting, or to reduce the cooking time of a casserole. Parboiling causes some losses of **vitamins** and **minerals**

through **leaching**, and some reduction of vitamins that are unstable at boiling point (e.g. **pantothenic acid**, **thiamin** and **vitamin C**). Parboiling of **beans** before using them in salads ensures that harmful **phytic acid** and **lectins** are destroyed. See also **blanching**.

Parmesan A variety of **cheese** which is very hard and pungent. It is always used finely grated and is an important feature in many Italian dishes. **Vegetarian** Parmesan is extremely difficult to obtain, but it is imported by a few specialist shops in larger cities. Strict vegetarians may prefer to use a different cheese or a **soya**-based Parmesan substitute, suitable for **vegans**, which is available from health-food shops.

parsley A small, European herbaceous plant, the curly, aromatic leaves of which are used as a **herb** and garnish. Parsley is readily available dried, but it can be grown quite easily at home for an abundant fresh supply.

USES: as a garnish, in parsley sauce and other sauces, and chopped into casseroles and soups. Parsley is said to stimulate the appetite and chewing a piece after eating **garlic** is said to help freshen the breath.

parsnip A long root vegetable with creamy-white flesh and a very strong, sweet flavour. Parsnips provide **starch** and **dietary fibre**. They also contain useful amounts of **folic acid**, **thiamin**, **niacin**, **pantothenic acid** and **vitamin C**. They will stay fresh for two weeks in a plastic bag stored in the refrigerator.

PREPARATION: top and tail, then scrub thoroughly. If the skin is rough it may be necessary to peel the parsnips and perhaps also to cut out the woody core. Boil until soft and mash with **butter**, or parboil and roast as you would potatoes. Alternatively, cut into chips or rings and deep fry.

USES: as a hot side vegetable or, once mashed, as an ingredient of a bake or **burgers**. Parsnips also go well in soups or diced in casseroles.

passion fruit (also called **granadilla** or **purple granadilla**) A small, wrinkled, olive-green or black tropical **fruit** with sweet, fragrant, yellow-white flesh containing crunchy, black, edible seeds. Passion fruit has a high **dietary fibre** content and also provides **sugars**, **vitamin C**, **potassium**, **magnesium** and **phosphorus**.

PREPARATION: cut in half and eat the flesh with a spoon, or scoop out the flesh.

USES: as a fresh fruit or to flavour home-made ice creams and sorbets. It also makes a colourful tangy sauce. The juice can be squeezed from the flesh and used in cocktails and punches.

pasta A dough traditionally made from **wheat flour** or **semolina** and water, sometimes with the addition of **eggs** and **milk**, moulded into a variety of shapes, such as **spaghetti** and **macaroni**, and sold fresh or dried. Pasta can be made using white or wholemeal flour, and can be coloured using **spinach**, **tomatoes** or other vegetables. In Italy a black pasta is available but this is coloured with squid ink, which may not be acceptable to **vegetarians**. **Organic** pasta is available, and pasta made from other **cereals** is also beginning to appear. Pasta is a good source of **protein**, **starch** and, if wholemeal, of **dietary fibre** and **B complex vitamins**.

PREPARATION: pasta is cooked in boiling water with a little **salt** until soft – but not disintegrating. It should be *al dente*, with a little bite to it. Some types of **lasagne** do not need to be pre-cooked before being assembled into a dish.

USES: pasta is traditionally eaten with a tomato, creamy **mushroom** or **cheese** sauce, or tossed in **pesto** or **olive oil** and **herbs**. It can also be baked in the sauce. Some types of pasta (such as shells and spirals) look attractive when used cold in salads. Some types of pasta can be added to soups, but be careful not to overcook.

pasteurization A mild form of heat treatment, which was named after its inventor Louis Pasteur (1822-1895). It is used to destroy bacteria in foods and to increase the keeping quality of foods. Pasteurization is used for foods such as **milk**, **beer** and **fruit juices**. Milk is heated to about 70°C for 15 seconds. This process does not stop milk from souring, but it does kill bacteria that might otherwise cause disease. Pasteurization of milk causes a 10% loss of the **B complex vitamins thiamin**, **pyridoxine**, **folic acid** and **vitamin B$_{12}$**, and a 25% loss of **vitamin C**. Non-pasteurized milk is available on a limited scale in some areas. See also **ultra heat treated**.

pastry A dough made from **flour**, water and **fat**, which may include other ingredients such as **eggs**, **sugar** or **cheese**. Vegetarians do not eat pastry that contains **lard** or **suet**. Any pastry products and ready-made frozen pastry must be checked to be sure they are made only with vegetable oils, vegetarian margarine or solid vegetable fat. Pastry is high in **starch** and contains varying amounts of fat. Pastry made with wholemeal flour provides more **dietary fibre**, **minerals** and **B complex vitamins** than pastry made with white, refined flour.

pattypan squash A round, flattish variety of **summer squash** with thin, easily blemished skin. When buying look for a tender, young pattypan, which should be quite small and firm, and with pale green skin that will turn white as it matures. It will keep for a few days in a plastic bag stored in the refrigerator.

PREPARATION: wash, then cut into pieces and steam until soft or sauté with **butter** or **olive oil** and fresh **herbs**. They may also be grated raw into salads, stewed, or stuffed like a **courgette** or **marrow**.

USES: as a hot side vegetable, in a casserole, stuffed with a savoury **nut** mixture or in a salad.

paw paw   See **papaya**.

pea

The bright green seed of the garden pea, which is eaten cooked as a **vegetable**. Garden peas provide more **protein**, **sugars**, **starch** and **dietary fibre** than most other common vegetables, and they also contain **calcium**, **iron**, **vitamin C**, **B complex vitamins** and some **molybdenum** and **manganese**. Dried peas and split dried peas, which may be soaked and cooked like fresh peas or soaked and allowed to sprout, contain only a small percentage of the vitamin C content of fresh peas.

PREPARATION: if you are able to obtain fresh young peas, shell them and boil them for approximately five minutes. Frozen peas may need to be cooked for five minutes. Dried peas need to be soaked overnight, rinsed and boiled in fresh water for 10 minutes. They can then be simmered for 45 minutes to an hour until soft.

USES: as a well-known, hot side vegetable, but cooked fresh peas may also be used cold in salads. Cooked dried peas can be used as a hot side vegetable too, or used to make an attractive warming soup. See also **split peas**.

pea bean   See **haricot bean**.

peach

A reddish-yellow, downy-skinned **fruit** with sweet, juicy, orange-yellow flesh. Peaches

179

contain some **sugars** along with reasonable amounts of **carotene**, **niacin** and **potassium**. They should be quite firm but have no trace of greenness on the skin. They will keep in the refrigerator for two to three days.

PREPARATION: peaches may be washed and eaten whole (apart from the stone). Alternatively, peel and serve in slices or chunks. Peach halves can be stuffed with **berries** and **cream**, and whole peaches stewed and cooked in pies and tarts.

USES: as a fresh-fruit dish, part of a fruit salad or in a hot fruit dessert. They are also good in jams or as a chilled soup.

peanut (also called **groundnut** or **monkey nut**) The seed of a small leguminous plant, which is strictly a **pulse** and not a **nut**. Peanuts are available in their shells or roasted and salted as a snack food. Those intended for cooking are best purchased in their shells, to ensure prime freshness.

Peanuts are rich in **protein** and **monounsaturated fats**, and provide reasonable amounts of **dietary fibre**. They also contain **potassium**, **calcium**, **magnesium**, **molybdenum**, **manganese**, **sulphur**, **thiamin**, **niacin**, **vitamin E**, **folic acid** and **pantothenic acid**, and small amounts of **zinc**, **iron** and **vitamin B₆**. Like most pulses, raw peanuts contain some **phytic acid** and toxic **lectins**, but these substances are broken down or destroyed by cooking or roasting.

PREPARATION: peanuts can be eaten as a snack or cocktail nibble, but they may also be chopped or ground to incorporate into a savoury bake, or puréed with oil and salt to make a **nut butter**.

USES: mainly as a snack food but can be used where mixed nuts are required in a savoury bake or in **burgers**, or in a sweet or savoury crumble topping.

pear A rounded or elongated bell-shaped **fruit** with thin, yellow, green or pinkish skin and juicy, sweet, white flesh that has a characteristically grainy texture. Pears are high in water and contain a little **dietary fibre** and **sugar**, a little **vitamin C** and negligible quantities of other vitamins and minerals.

When buying select pears that are firm and free from any blemishes. They may be eaten when still firm or allowed to ripen in a warm place for two or three days until the flesh near the stalk gives when pressed gently.

PREPARATION: pears can be eaten fresh like **apples** or served in slices. They can also be diced and used in fruit pies or peeled and baked or poached in red **wine**.

USES: as a fresh fruit or as part of a fruit salad or hot fruit dish. They are especially attractive baked and dipped in melted chocolate or **carob**.

pearl barley Seeds of **barley** that have been milled to remove the outer husk, bran and germ.

Pearl barley contains small amounts of **phosphorus, zinc, niacin, vitamin E, vitamin B$_6$, folic acid** and **pantothenic acid**, but much of the **B complex vitamin** content is destroyed in cooking. It lacks the **dietary fibre** content and the texture of whole (**pot** or Scotch) barley, but it is very easy to digest.

PREPARATION: soak for an hour in hot water and then add to simmering casseroles and soups and cook until tender.

USES: mainly as a thickener for soups and casseroles, or cooked in **milk** as a gentle food for those recovering from illness. It can also be used to make barley water.

pecan nut The smooth, dark red **nut** of the pecan tree, native to North America, with an oily kernel which looks and tastes similar to a **walnut**. It is high in **unsaturated fats** and provides some **protein** and small amounts of **iron, zinc, manganese** and **B complex vitamins**.

PREPARATION: shell and chop.

USES: good in sweet dishes such as the great American favourite pecan pie. Pecan nuts can also be used like walnuts in fruit cakes.

pectin A non-starch polysaccharide present in fruit and vegetables, particularly **root vegetables** such as **parsnips, swedes, turnips** and **yams**. Pectin forms a stiff gel under certain conditions and this property is important in jam making, and explains the use of pectin as a gelling agent in a number of manufactured foods.

It is claimed by some that pectin may help lower high levels of **cholesterol** in the blood and to slow down the absorption of **glucose** into the blood.

penne A variety of **pasta** shaped as a tube cut at a slant, to represent an old fashioned pen nib.

peppercorns The black or white dried **fruit** of a tropical climbing vine native to India, which is used whole or ground as a **spice**. Black peppercorns are picked just before they are quite ripe and dried in the sun. White peppercorns are allowed to ripen and are soaked and rubbed to remove their husks. Black and white peppercorns can be ground in a peppermill to yield fresh pepper. See also **black pepper**.

peppermint A variety of **mint**.

peppermint tea A refreshing infusion made from the leaves of the peppermint plant. It is one of the most widely available and popular of commercially produced **herbal teas**. Mint contains menthol, which is considered by some to have a number of beneficial effects on the digestive system, such as stimulating the appetite.

peppers (also called **pimientos** or **sweet peppers**) Crisp green (unripe) red, yellow or orange bell-shaped **fruits** of a species of capsicum. Peppers are a very good source of **vitamin C** and **carotene**, although the vitamin C content is depleted in cooking. When buying peppers look for firm and smooth ones. They should be stored in the refrigerator and will keep for one or two days after they have been cut.

PREPARATION: slice in half and cut away the stalk and white pith and bitter seeds. Peppers can be **blanched** for three minutes in boiling water and refreshed in cold water before they are stuffed and baked.

The skins can be removed by baking the peppers in a medium oven for 15–20 minutes until the skin is charred. Once cooled, the skin will peel easily. Peeling peppers is unnecessary for most recipes.

USES: cut into shapes for a colourful garnish or addition to a stir-fry. Raw peppers are an excellent addition to a salad. They may also be stuffed with a **cereal**, **nut** or **cheese** mixture and baked. Peppers are an essential ingredient in many casseroles, and are also used in **quiches**, stuffed pancakes, Italian dishes and Mexican tapas.

pepsin An **enzyme** derived from the stomachs of pigs, sometimes used with **rennet** in the manufacture of **cheese**. Pepsin is not suitable for vegetarians.

perpetual spinach See **spinach beet**.

persimmon (also called **kaki fruit**) A large, orange-red tropical **fruit** (similar to a large tomato) with tough skin and sharp, orange flesh. The flesh is bitter unless the fruit is fully ripe. Persimmons can be kept in a plastic bag in a warm place until the skin becomes translucent and the fruit gives slightly when pressed.

PREPARATION: cut off the top of the fruit, scoop out the flesh with a spoon and discard the seeds.

USES: as an unusual fruit salad ingredient or serve with **yoghurt** or **cream**. See also **sharon fruit**.

pesto An aromatic sauce made with fresh **basil**, **garlic** and **pine kernels**, which is most often used in small quantities to accompany **pasta** dishes. Pesto sauce is commonly made using non-vegetarian **Parmesan** cheese, although brands made with vegetarian **cheese** and made without cheese are available from health-food shops.

petit pois A variety of garden **pea** that produces tiny, sweet peas.

phosphorus A non-metallic **mineral** that is vital to the formation of strong bones and teeth, and also plays an important role in the release and storage of energy in the body. It is a key constituent of the sheath that protects the nerve fibres, and it helps maintain the correct pH balance in different parts of the body.

Phosphorus is found in all foods with the exception of **fats**, **oils** and **sugar**. Particularly good vegetarian sources are **dairy products**, **lentils**, wholegrain **bread**, **eggs** and **yeast extract**. Diets that contain sufficient **protein** and **calcium** will contain enough phosphorus. Deficiency of phosphorus alone from an inadequate diet rarely occurs in humans.

physalis   See **cape gooseberry**.

phytic acid   A compound of inositol and **phosphorus**, found chiefly in wholegrain **cereals**, **nuts** and **pulses**. It readily combines with essential minerals (e.g. **calcium**, **iron**, **magnesium** and **zinc**) during digestion and inhibits their absorption by the body. The body can adapt to a high phytic acid intake in the diet by increasing the amount of phytase, an enzyme present in the intestine, so that after a time the binding effect of phytic acid is reduced. Phytic acid is also broken down by enzymes in **yeast** during proving and baking of **bread**, and in pulses when they are rinsed thoroughly and soaked in water. Unleavened breads, such as **pitta bread**, may contain phytic acid.

pimiento   See **peppers**.

pineapple   A large tropical **fruit** with tough, scratchy skin and fibrous, juicy, yellow flesh. Pineapples are a good source of **vitamin C** and also contain **sugars**, **potassium**, **magnesium** and **dietary fibre**. Canned pineapples contain only half the potassium, magnesium and vitamin C of the fresh fruit, and if canned in syrup they contain nearly twice the **sugar**.

Always ensure that pineapples are ripe when they are purchased, because they do not ripen at home. They should smell sweet and the leaves should be stiff.

PREPARATION: the easiest way to prepare a pineapple is to cut it into slices and then into pieces, discarding the inner core and the skin.

USES: in a fresh-fruit salad or hot fruit pudding, a sorbet, a cheesecake or a pineapple upsidedown cake. Pineapples can be used in stir-fries and sweet-and-sour dishes and to top pizza. They can also be used to make jam. Hollowed out pineapples make a good serving vessel for a fruit salad.

pine kernel (also called **pine nut**) The oily, aromatic seed of certain varieties of pine tree. Pine kernels are high in **fat**, mainly **monounsaturated fats**, and also provide some **dietary fibre**, **protein**, **B complex vitamins** and **vitamin E**. Because of their high fat content they may become rancid if kept for too long or stored in a warm place.

PREPARATION: as with **nuts**, pine kernels may be chopped, ground, toasted or roasted under the grill, in a heavy pan or in the oven. They can be baked in savoury dishes or eaten raw.

USES: the most important use for pine kernels is to make **pesto** sauce. They are also good mixed with **rice** or other **grains**, to stuff vegetables, and may be sprinkled on salads.

pink bean   See **borlotti bean**.

pink grapefruit   A variety of **grapefruit** with pink flesh.

pinto bean   A variety of **kidney bean** with a cream-coloured, brown-speckled skin and a delicate, sweet flavour.

PREPARATION: soak overnight, rinse thoroughly and bring to the boil in fresh water. Boil for 10 minutes and then simmer for an hour to an hour and a half until tender.

USES: pinto beans can be used in place of red kidney beans or **haricot beans** in a recipe. They make a colourful addition to a cold bean salad.

pistachio nut   The characteristically green, **almond**-flavoured fruit kernel of a small, west Asian tree related to the **cashew**. They are high in **unsaturated fats** and also provide **protein**, **iron**, **calcium**, **phosphorus**, **potassium**, **manganese** and some **B complex vitamins** and **vitamin E**. Salted pistachios are high in **sodium**. To ensure prime freshness it is best to buy unshelled pistachio nuts.

PREPARATION: after shelling, pistachios can be chopped, ground or roasted under the grill or in the oven.

USES: they are a useful colouring ingredient for ice cream, fruit salads and **milk** puddings, and they also make a decorative garnish.

pitagna (also called **surinam cherry**) A small, red, deeply ridged **fruit** related to the **clove**, which is grown in Israel and New Zealand.

PREPARATION: it can be eaten fresh, like a **cherry**, or cut open to remove the several pips.

USES: although pitagna may be eaten fresh, it is best used in preserves.

pitta bread A flat, rounded, unleavened Middle Eastern **bread** made with either brown or white **flour**, and sometimes available flavoured with **herbs**, **garlic** or **chilli powder**. Because pitta bread is unleavened it may contain **phytic acid**, which can interfere with and inhibit the absorption of certain minerals.

PREPARATION: pitta bread is hollow and can be halved to make pockets or opened out. It can be eaten cold or warmed in an oven.

USES: serve with a curry in place of or with **rice**, or with any other casserole dish. Use to make a pitta pocket sandwich stuffed with salad, Middle Eastern **falafel** balls and **hummus**, or grated **cheese**. Cut into fingers and serve with a paté or with crudities and dips, or with a soup. Can also be used as a quick pizza base.

plantain A variety of large **banana**, that is cooked and eaten when green, and is sometimes called the 'cooking banana'. Plantains have a high **starch** content, provide some **dietary fibre**, small amounts of **protein** and negligible amounts of **micronutrients**.

PREPARATION: plantains are always cooked before eating. Peel, then boil and mash or slice and deep fry, steam or roast.

USES: plantains are commonly used in West Indian and Rastafarian cookery.

plant milk An old name for **soya milk**.

pleurotte See **oyster mushroom**.

plum A small, thin-skinned, purple, green or yellow **fruit** with sweet, fibrous, yellow or pinkish flesh. There are many varieties of plum. Dessert plums are best for eating raw as they have a higher **sugar** content. Plums contain **dietary fibre**, **potassium**, **carotene** and a little **vitamin C**.

Plums should be quite firm and have a distinctive bloom on their skins. Unripe plums can be left to ripen for one or two days.

PREPARATION: wash, halve, remove the stone and stew, with or without skins, in a little water with **sugar** or **honey** to taste.

USES: in pies and tarts or stewed and served with custard or **yoghurt**. Plums are often used to make preserves.

plum tomato   A variety of **tomato** grown in Italy, which is commonly bought canned in this country and used to make soups and in casseroles.

polenta   A traditional, north Italian food made from a porridge of **corn meal**, which is cooked until it thickens and then allowed to cool in a shallow tin until it has set. It is then cut into squares, dipped in beaten egg and corn meal, and deep-fried. Polenta is usually served with a tomato sauce.

polyunsaturated fats   All **fats** and **oils** are made up in varying proportions of saturated fats, **mono-unsaturated fats** and polyunsaturated fats. Saturated fats contain mainly saturated fatty acids and tend to be solid at room temperature. Polyunsaturated fats contain mainly polyunsaturated fatty acids and tend to be liquid at room temperature.

Saturated fats, which frequently come from animal foods, including **cheese**, **milk** and **eggs**, are thought to raise blood **cholesterol**. Polyunsaturated fats, which occur in many **nuts**, **seeds** and vegetable **oils**, can help to lower blood cholesterol. Monounsaturated fats, for example **olive oil**, have a neutral effect on blood cholesterol.

pomegranate   A round tropical **fruit** with hard, reddish skin and juicy, pink flesh made up of many small, crisp, seed-bearing pods. Pomegranates contain **sugars** and **potassium**, but only a little **vitamin C**.

When buying pomegranates look for firm fruits. They will keep for up to a week if stored in the refrigerator.

PREPARATION: cut away the skin with a knife. The flavour is best if the flesh is eaten raw. The seeds are edible but they have a bitter taste. To extract the juice from a pomegranate, make a small hole in the skin and gently squeeze the fruit.

USES: the flesh may be served in a fruit salad or used to flavour a sorbet. The juice can be used in cocktails and is the basis of grenadine.

pomelo (also called **shaddock**) A large **citrus fruit** with an elongated top and thick, yellow or yellow-green skin. It is the original parent of the modern **grapefruit**. The texture of the pomelo is more coarse than that of the grapefruit, but the flavour is less bitter.

PREPARATION: peel away the thick skin and remove the bitter skin around each segment.

USES: as an alternative to grapefruit for breakfast, a starter or in a fruit salad. The peel can also be candied.

poor man's asparagus See **Good King Henry**.

poppy seed The tiny, round, blue-black seed of the poppy flower. Poppy seeds are rich in **polyunsaturated fats** and contain reasonable amounts of other nutrients, although since they are eaten in small quantities their nutritional contribution to the diet is negligible. They have a nutty, slightly smoky flavour and should be stored in a sealed container in a cool place.

USES: use in baking, in cakes, breads and biscuits or as a decoration. Sprinkle over cooked vegetables, soft **cheeses** or salads, or add to salad dressing.

porcini A variety of wild **mushroom** of the boletus family, native to Italy. It is related to the French **cèpes** and Japanese **shitake** mushrooms. Porcini have soft, edible stems and a woody flavour.

potassium A **mineral** found in the fluids within cells and essential for healthy cell function. In conjunction with **sodium**, it regulates the levels of acidity and alkalinity in the body and helps maintain the correct water balance. It is an important factor in the functioning of nerves and muscles. Potassium is found in nearly all foods except **sugar**, **fats** and **oils**, but particularly good vegetarian sources include green leafy **vegetables**, **mushrooms**, **bananas**, **potatoes**, **grapes**, **tomatoes** and **brewer's yeast**. There are no losses on baking or steaming but boiling vegetables can cause up to 50% loss, although this can be recovered in the cooking water. Potassium deficiency due to inadequate intake is rare.

potato A starchy white tuber with brown or red skin, eaten as a **vegetable**. Potatoes are a staple part of the British diet and contribute significantly to nutritional intake. They contain **starch** and **dietary fibre**, and small amounts of **protein, potassium, thiamin, niacin** and **vitamin B$_6$**. They are an important source of **vitamin C**, supplying 20% of the total intake in the average UK diet.

Potatoes that are not stored correctly in a dark, dry, cool place develop green patches, which contain a toxic substance called solanine. Solanine also appears when old potatoes begin to sprout. It should be avoided as it causes nausea, vomiting and abdominal pain.

PREPARATION: new potatoes can be scrubbed and used in their skins. Older potatoes should be peeled. Potatoes can be boiled, baked, mashed, fried as chips, or diced and added to hearty casseroles and soups. Potatoes should not be eaten raw.

USES: as a side vegetable or mashed, grated or sliced as a pie topping. Boiled potatoes can be used cold in salads. Potatoes can be puréed and shaped into gnocchi to serve with an Italian-style tomato sauce. Grated potato can be shaped into cakes and fried or added to pancake batter.

potato flour A starchy, **gluten**-free **flour** derived from **potatoes**. It is available from some health-food shops or by mail-order from specialist outlets.

USES: as a thickener in soups and casseroles, or in pastry and baked goods.

pot barley (also called **Scotch barley**) Barley grain that is sold whole, unlike **pearl barley**, which is milled to remove the husk, bran and germ. Pot barley is richer in **dietary fibre** and in **B complex vitamins** than pearl barley, and retains its shape better during cooking. It has a chewy texture.

PREPARATION: bring to the boil and then simmer, covered, for two hours in four times its volume of water.

USES: in soups (especially Scotch broth) casseroles or stuffed vegetables, or cold in salads.

pregnancy It is possible to be **vegetarian** throughout pregnancy. All pregnant women are advised to ensure that their diets are properly balanced and provide an adequate intake of all **vitamins** and **minerals**, **folic acid**, **protein** and **energy**. See INTRODUCTION, SPECIAL NEEDS, PREGNANCY.

prickly pear (also called **cactus fruit**) The oval **fruit** of the opuntia cactus, with cream, orange or pink skin and a sweet pulp full of hard but edible seeds. It has sweet-tasting but rather bland flesh, with a melon-like aroma. When buying, look for fruit with a deep, even colour and which gives slightly to pressure. Ripe fruit will keep in the refrigerator for up to a week.

PREPARATION: prickly pears should not be handled too much as their surfaces are dotted with clusters of tiny, hooked spines. Cut in half using a knife and fork, and scoop out the flesh.

USES: in a sorbet or fruit salad, or with **yoghurt** or **cream**.

protein Essential components of all living matter, made up of long chains of individual units called amino acids. The cells of our bones, muscles, skin, nails, hair and every other tissue are made up of proteins, as are vital fluids such as blood, enzymes and hormones. Protein is constantly being broken down into its component amino acids during digestion, then absorbed and rearranged into new body protein.

Of the 20 or so amino acids, eight are called essential amino acids because they cannot be synthesized by the body and must be obtained from foods. Foods that contain all eight of these essential amino acids in the proportions required by the body are said to provide high-quality protein. High-quality protein is usually found in animal foods. Although meat and fish are unsuitable for **vegetarians**, foods such as **eggs**, **dairy products**, **nuts**, **pulses** and **beans** are also good sources of protein. **Vegans** and those who eat little dairy food often plan their meals to combine two 'incomplete' sources of protein to complement each other, for example, **beans** and **grains**. Such a protein-combining meal might be baked beans on wholegrain toast. It is now thought less important to obtain all amino acids at one meal than it is to ensure a regular and varied intake of protein.

prune A dried **plum**. Traditionally prunes are dried on the tree, but nowadays they are more likely to be artificially dried. Prunes provide **sugars**, **dietary fibre**, **potassium**, **calcium**, **carotene**, **vitamin A** and **iron**. They are often used as a mild laxative because of the high concentration of dietary fibre and the presence of a substance called diphenylisatin.

PREPARATION: like all **dried fruits**, prunes can be rehydrated by soaking them overnight. This also dilutes their taste and may make them more palatable. They may also be stewed.

USES: with breakfast **muesli** or at the end of a meal perhaps with custard or **cream**. Prunes can be used in a hot winter fruit **compote**, in cakes and flapjacks.

pudding rice A variety of **short-grain rice** produced in Italy with sweet-tasting, chalky grains, which cling together on cooking. It is used for puddings and sweets.

pulse (also called **legume**) The edible **seeds** of leguminous plants, such as **beans**, **peas** and **lentils**. Pulses are an important vegetarian source of **protein** and they also contain **starch** and **dietary fibre**. With the exception of **soya**, they are low in **fat**. Pulses are rich in **calcium**, **thiamin**, **riboflavin** and **niacin**, and also contain some **iron**, **molybdenum**, **manganese** and **carotene**. If they are washed and soaked for a few days, many pulses can be eaten as

bean sprouts, which have the additional benefit of being rich in **vitamin C**. The seed pods of some leguminous plants (such as **French beans**, **mange-tout** and **runner beans**) are eaten when they are unripe and the seeds are only very small. They, therefore, provide proportionately less of the above nutrients and more dietary fibre. Most pulses contain small amounts of **phytic acid** and toxic **lectins**, which are broken down when the pulses are cooked or sprouted.

pumpkin A large, round, American winter **squash** with a tough, orange or green rind and pulpy, orange flash. Pumpkins have a high water content and are therefore low in Calories, and are a good source of **carotene**. A pumpkin with firm, unblemished skin should be stored in a cool, dry, dark place for up to two months.

PREPARATION: pumpkins may be sliced into segments, peeled and the seeds and fibrous pulp scooped out. The flesh may then be steamed, baked, simmered in water, or added to a casserole or soups. Pumpkins can also be hollowed out to make decorative skin tureens.

USES: pumpkin flesh can be sweetened and used in pumpkin pie, or a sweet pudding. It can be served as a savoury side vegetable, mashed or puréed with **butter** and **spices**. It can be used in West Indian-style casseroles and also makes a colourful soup.

pumpkin seed The large, smooth, green **seed** of the **pumpkin**. They can be obtained in their shells from pumpkins or purchased ready shelled. Pumpkin seeds are high in **polyunsaturated fats**, **protein**, **B complex vitamins** and **iron**.

PREPARATION: pumpkin seeds can be used as they are or toasted in a heavy frying pan, perhaps with a little **soya sauce**. Seeds saved from a pumpkin need to be toasted until their shells burst and then they can be extracted.

USES: as a savoury nibble or sprinkled onto salads or cooked vegetables to add protein to the meal. They may also be used in **muesli**.

purple granadilla See **passion fruit**.

purple sprouting broccoli A popular variety of **broccoli** that yields many small, purple florets, which turn green when cooked.

puy lentil A variety of **lentil** originating from Puy in France. They are smaller than other lentils and have a distinctive grey-green colour. Puy lentils can sometimes be found in health-food shops and are interchangeable in cooking with **brown lentils**.

PREPARATION: soak overnight, rinse and bring to the boil in fresh water. Boil for 10 minutes and then simmer for 30 minutes until soft. Alternatively, puy lentils can be cooked without soaking.

Again they must be boiled for 10 minutes and should then be simmered for an hour to an hour and a half.

USES: puy lentils may be used in any recipe which requires brown lentils. They are particularly good in vegetable Cornish pasties, shepherds pie and **burgers**.

pyridoxine   See **vitamin B₆**.

quark   A very low-**fat** soft **cheese** made with **skimmed milk** and without **salt**. **Animal rennet** is not used in its manufacture and quark is, therfore, generally suitable for vegetarians.

USES: in cheesecakes and creamy sauces, or as an alternative to **cream** with fruit or a rich dessert.

Queensland nut   See **macadamia nut**.

quince   A pear-shaped, aromatic, hard **fruit** with thin, yellow skin and white flesh that is too acidic to eat raw. Quinces are not often commercially available today. They contain large quantities of **pectin** as well as **sugars**, **dietary fibre**, **potassium** and small amounts of **vitamin C**. Store away from other foods as the strong perfume may taint them.

PREPARATION: peel, core and chop the flesh. It can then be stewed in a little water with **sugar** or **honey** to taste.

USES: mainly in preserves, especially quince jelly. Also in fruity sauces or combined with **apples** in a pie.

quinoa A tiny, yellow **cereal** native to South America. A relative newcomer to the UK and although nutritional information about it is scarce it appears to be rich in **protein**, **iron** and **B complex vitamins**. The grains hold their shape well in cooking, have a sweet taste and are easy to digest.

PREPARATION: the grains must be washed before use as they are coated with a bitter natural chemical to deter predators. Once washed the grains are cooked like **rice** in twice their volume of water for around 15 minutes. Washed and dried grains can be ground in a coffee grinder to yield a sweet **flour**.

USES: serve as a side grain like rice, or use to stuff vegetables or cold in a salad. Quinoa flour can be used with wheat **flour** in **bread** and biscuits.

Quorn A vegetable **protein** which is now becoming widely available as a **meat substitute**. The manufacturing process involves a **fungus** related to the **mushroom**. Quorn has a fibrous texture and a pale colour and is sold chilled in pieces which look rather like cooked chicken, or made up into convenience foods. It has little flavour of its own, but it will absorb the flavours of foods that it is cooked with. Because Quorn contains **battery eggs** it is not considered to be suitable for **vegetarians** by the Vegetarian Society.

PREPARATION: chilled pieces of Quorn may be used in much the same way as one might use meat.

USES: in casseroles, curries and stir-fries.

radicchio A variety of **chicory** with red, sometimes white, crisp leaves that have a slightly bitter flavour. They are normally sold ready washed and prepared, sometimes with a variety of other salad leaves, in plastic bags which will store for two to three days in the refrigerator.

PREPARATION: rinse in cold water as you would **lettuce** and pat dry with kitchen towels or use a salad spinner.

USES: normally in combination with **lettuce**, **Chinese leaf**, **curly endive** and other salad vegetables in a mixed salad. Radicchio leaves are often also used as a garnish.

radish Any of several varieties of small, rounded roots, used as a salad **vegetable**. Radishes may be red (the most common), white or black and have pungent, white flesh. They have a high water content and are low in **protein** and **sugars**. They contain no **fat** but provide small amounts of **iron**, **copper**, **vitamin C** and **folic acid**. However, they are eaten in such small quantities that they make a negligible contribution to the diet. Radishes will stay fresh for a week in a plastic bag stored in the refrigerator.

PREPARATION: radishes can be sliced or grated into salads, or used as a garnish. To make a radish rose, trim the stalk end and make several cuts towards the root. Leave the cut radish in a bowl of iced water for 30 minutes to open out. Radishes can also be used in stir-fries or peeled, sliced and boiled in salted water, or pickled.

USES: mainly with salads or as a garnish, but they may also be used as a hot side vegetable, perhaps in a white sauce.

raisin A dried, black, seedless **grape**. Raisins are high in **dietary fibre** and **potassium**, and they also contain small quantities of **iron**, **calcium**, **magnesium** and other **micronutrients**. They are frequently sold coated with mineral oil to give them an attractive shiny appearance and to prevent them from clumping together, though some health-food shops sell raisins that have not been treated in this way.

PREPARATION: raisins coated with mineral oils should be washed thoroughly before use. Raisins can be soaked in water or **fruit juice** to make them plump, and puréed to a sweet paste.

USES: raisins are used in cakes, biscuits, **muesli** and in some salads, as well as being eaten as a snack food, sometimes coated in **carob**, chocolate or **yoghurt**.

rambutan A plum-sized **fruit** related to the **lychee**. It is covered in long, green, curved spines (which turn red when the fruit is ripe) and the flesh inside is white and translucent.

PREPARATION: break open the spiny covering to reach the white flesh and then strip the flesh away from the central stone.

USES: once removed from their shell, rambutans can be eaten like plums or the flesh can be used in fruit salads, perhaps as a contrast to a darker fruit.

rapeseed oil A vegetable **oil** extracted from the seeds of the yellow-flowered rape plant. Rapeseed oil is high in **monounsaturated fats** and can be used as a cooking oil or as part of a salad dressing.

raspberry A small, juicy, red **fruit** of the raspberry shrub made up of many, tiny, soft seed pods around a white core. Raspberries are lower in **sugars** than most other fruits, with the exception of **gooseberries** and certain **melons**. They also contain a useful amount of **vitamin C** and **dietary fibre**, with some **iron**, **potassium**, **pantothenic acid** and **biotin**. Freezing raspberries does not significantly impair their nutritional value, but they will not stay fresh in the refrigerator for more than one day.

PREPARATION: do not wash unless absolutely necessary as this may reduce their flavour.

USES: raspberries can be used as a fresh fruit with **cream**, in a fruit salad or as a gateau or pavlova filling. They can be cooked and sieved to make a bright red sauce to serve with ice cream, or used in wine and jam making.

raspberry vinegar   A variety of **wine vinegar** flavoured with raspberries, which has an unusual and delicate flavour. It is used in salad dressings.

ravioli   A variety of **pasta** made up of small squares of **lasagne** crimped together around a small amount of filling. Vegetarian fillings, for example, might be a mixture of curd **cheese** and grated **nuts**, or **ricotta cheese** and **spinach**. Ravioli is cooked like other pasta shapes in boiling salted water and can be served with **oil** and **herbs**, **butter**, or a sauce. It can be purchased in chilled packs or made at home.

ready-made meals   There is a wide selection of chilled, frozen and vacuum-packed ready meals that are suitable for vegetarians. The range includes **burgers**, curries, **pasta** dishes, **quiches** and vegetable dishes, and there are also special vegetarian meals for slimmers. However, some may contain non-vegetarian **cheese**, **battery eggs** or non-vegetarian food **additives**. Foods that have been verified suitable for vegetarians by the Vegetarian Society carry a 'V symbol' seedling logo. Other logos may not represent the same standards. Ready-made dishes can be a help to vegetarians who do not have the time to make meals from scratch, though some vegetarians prefer to aim for an additive-free wholefood diet.

red cabbage   A variety of **cabbage** with tightly furled, dark red leaves and a large, firm heart. Its nutritional profile is similar to other varieties of cabbage, providing **folic acid**, **potassium** and **vitamin C**. Red cabbage wrapped in clingfilm in the refrigerator will stay fresh for one week.

PREPARATION: raw red cabbage can be shredded for use in salads, or it can be boiled, braised or pickled.

USES: red cabbage can be used in place of (or with) shredded **white salad cabbage** in coleslaw and other salads. It is a popular candidate for pickling and can also be cooked and eaten as a hot side vegetable or used in a soup. In Germany it is braised with **butter**, **sugar**, **onions**, **vinegar** and sliced **apple**.

redcurrant A small, round, shiny, red **fruit** which grows in bunches and is related to the **gooseberry** and **blackcurrant**. Redcurrants are a good source of **dietary fibre** because of their edible seeds, and they are also high in **vitamin C**. They also contain some **potassium**, **carotene** and **biotin**, but not as much as blackcurrants. Redcurrants are seasonally available in July and August and may be stored in the refrigerator for up to two weeks or frozen.

PREPARATION: wash gently in cold water. The fruits can be stripped from the main stem with a fork. It is a matter of taste whether or not to remove the tiny stems. Redcurrants can be served raw or they may be stewed.

USES: as a fresh fruit, in a salad or as a garnish. Redcurrants are traditionally used in summer pudding and to make redcurrant jelly. They can also be baked in pies or tarts, or puréed and sieved to make a bright red, sweet or tart sauce.

red wine vinegar A variety of **wine vinegar** made with red wine.

rennet An enzyme used to separate **milk** in the manufacturing of **cheese**. Its source affects the suitability of the cheese for vegetarians. See **animal rennet**; **genetically engineered rennet**; **microbial rennet**.

residues Traces of agricultural chemicals (fertilizers, pesticides, fungicides) which may remain in intensively farmed produce after it has been harvested. Today, many people who are concerned about the levels and potential adverse effects of residues in foods prefer to buy **organic foods** wherever possible.

retinol The chemical name for **vitamin A**. Vitamin A can also be obtained from **carotene**. In general, retinol is found in animal foods and carotene is found in plant foods.

rhubarb The crisp, pink, sour stalk of the rhubarb plant, which is treated as a **fruit**. It is very high in water and contains only small amounts of

207

dietary fibre, **protein** or **sugars** and few **micronutrients**. It does contain relatively large amounts of **calcium**, but because rhubarb also contains **oxalic acid** this is not easily absorbed by the body. The leaves should not be eaten as they contain toxic levels of oxalic acid. Rhubarb is in season between February and mid-summer.

PREPARATION: forced rhubarb is thin, pale and more tender than sticks that are allowed to mature naturally. It should be trimmed, chopped into pieces and stewed with **sugar** and **spices** until tender. Older rhubarb may need to be peeled as the skin can be stringy.

USES: as it has a bitter taste in its raw state, rhubarb is most commonly served stewed and sweetened, often with custard. It can be served cold with **cream**, used in a pie or fruit crumble, or in preserves.

riboflavin (also called **vitamin B₂**) One of the **B complex vitamins** needed for the release of energy from food. It is found in a wide range of foods, but particularly good vegetarian sources are **yeast extract**, **brewer's yeast**, **soya beans**, **dairy products** and **eggs**.

rice A **cereal** available in a number of varieties. Brown rice contains more **dietary fibre** than **white rice** and also provides the **B complex vitamins**. White rice is less nutritious, but easier to digest and quicker to prepare. The cooking time depends on the variety.

PREPARATION: rice is cooked in boiling water for between 10–40 minutes, and it can also be cooked inside the oven. For convenience, rice is available precooked and canned, chilled, frozen or dried. Rice should be stored in a cool, dry place in a sealed container. It has a long shelf life, making it possible to keep several varieties available for a number of different uses.

USES: rice may be used as a side dish, or in main course savouries. It can be used in salads and to stuff vegetables, and in sweet puddings. See **basmati rice**; **glutinous rice**; **ground rice**; **jasmine rice**; **long-grain rice**; **pudding rice**; **risotto rice**; **short-grain rice**.

rice flour A **gluten**-free **flour**, which can be ground from either white or brown **rice**, and is a popular substitute for ordinary flour among those who have an allergy to wheat gluten.

USES: to make gluten-free baked goods.

ricotta cheese A type of white **cheese** with a soft, moist, spongy texture, similar to but smoother than cottage cheese, and a mildly sweet taste. Unlike most other cheeses, ricotta is made from the **whey** rather than the curds of separated **milk**. Ricotta cheese made with **animal rennet** is widely available.

PREPARATION: it is frequently used mashed with **herbs** added for flavouring.

USES: mashed ricotta can be used as a filling for pancakes and **pasta** tubes or parcels (e.g. **ravioli**).

rigatone   A variety of **pasta** in the shape of large, ridged tubes. It often features in baked pasta dishes.

risotto rice (also called **arborio rice**)   A variety of **white rice** with medium-sized grains, between long and short grain. It is named after the dish that it is traditionally used to make. Risotto rice absorbs more water than **long-grain** rice and during cooking **starch** is released which gives the risotto a creamy texture.

PREPARATION: gently sauté the rice in **butter** or **oil** and **onion** and **spices** before adding the cooking water. A litre of water will be absorbed by 250 g of risotto rice during cooking, twice as much as white, long-grain rice. The water has to be added gradually over the cooking time of 30 minutes. Risotto rice is not suitable for cooking in the oven.

USES: a speciality rice that is especially suited for making risotto dishes.

roasted buckwheat   See **kasha**; **buckwheat**.

roasting   A method of cooking in the oven using radiant heat. Roasting is commonly used to cook meat, but it can also be used to cook vegetarian foods. Only those **vitamins** that are sensitive to high temperatures, such as **vitamin C**, **thiamin** and

pantothenic acid, are likely to be lost in roasting. Although some nutrients may **leach** out as some vegetable juices are lost, it is inadvisable to make a sauce with the juices as they will be mixed with the large amounts of oil used in roasting.

rocket (also called **arugula**) A salad vegetable that is a member of the **mustard** family. It has long, toothed leaves that look similar to **dandelion** leaves and have a peppery flavour. Rocket has, to a degree, fallen out of use, but it is still available from most supermarkets.
PREPARATION: trim the bases of the leaves, wash in cold water and pat dry or use a salad spinner.
USES: mainly in mixed-leaf salads.

rock melon A variety of **melon** that is small and oval with ribbed, rough, beige-coloured skin and sweet, orange flesh.

rolled oats See **oats**.

romaine lettuce See **cos lettuce**.

root vegetable A plant that is grown for its edible roots or tubers. Root vegetables are often high in starchy complex **carbohydrates** and in **dietary fibre**, and tend to be a staple food during the winter months. See **batata**; **beetroot**; **carrot**; **cassava**; **daikon**; **horseradish**; **Jerusalem artichoke**;

jicama; kumara; lotus root; malanga; parsnip; pink fir apple; potato; radish; salsify; scorzonera; swede; taro; turnip.

Roquefort A French **cheese** made from **ewes' milk**.

rose coco bean A pink-skinned variety of **kidney bean**.

rosehip tea A variety of **herbal tea** that is made from rosehips, which are the berry-like fruits of certain types of rose. In the UK, rosehip tea is one of the most popular and widely available of commercially-prepared herbal teas. It has a fruity taste and is high in **vitamin C**.

rosemary The aromatic, grey-green, needle-like leaves of a small European shrub, used fresh or dried, whole or powdered, as a **herb**. Dried rosemary should be stored in an airtight container in a cool, dry place.
  USES: rosemary is traditionally associated with lamb dishes. Vegetarians, however, may use it to flavour stuffed vegetables, **nut roasts**, **tomato** sauces or **bean** casseroles.

rowanberry The orange-scarlet, berry-like fruit of the mountain ash tree. Rowanberries are not sold commercially but can be harvested from the wild in October, when they are coloured but not soft.

PREPARATION: like all **wild foods** rowanberries must be washed thoroughly. Remove the stalks and simmer in water, then strain them to produce a juice.

USES: the juice is traditionally used almost exclusively to make a jelly by heating the juice with **sugar**. The jelly is served with game, lamb and poultry, but vegetarians may enjoy it with a **nut roast** or to give flavour to a gravy or sauce.

royal jelly   A substance secreted by worker bees as a food for the larvae, particularly those larvae destined to become queen bees. Royal jelly contains the **B complex vitamins** and is popular as a food supplement, available in pure liquid form, blended with **honey** or in capsules (these capsules, however, are often made of **gelatine**). Although a rich source of food for the queen bee, its contribution to a human diet is negligible.

runner bean   (also called **scarlet runner**)   The fibrous, immature pods of the scarlet runner bean plant, classed as a **pulse**. Runner beans are high in water and low in most **micronutrients** although they are a good source of **carotene** and **dietary fibre**. They can be stored in a basket in the kitchen for three to four days or in a plastic bag in the refrigerator for up to a week.

PREPARATION: runner beans must not be eaten raw as they contain toxic **lectins** and **phytic acid**. They should be washed thoroughly, then topped

213

and tailed, and the stringy edges pulled away.
They can be cooked whole or chopped into bite-
sized pieces and boiled in salted water for between
five and seven minutes.

USES: as a hot side vegetable, perhaps in a **cheese**
sauce, or, cooled, in bean salads.

rutabaga See **swede**.

rye A **cereal** grown in cold climates and used
primarily to make whisky and **flour**, although rye
flakes and whole grains are also available from
health-food shops. Rye has a strong savoury flavour and is rich in **protein**, **B complex vitamins**, **calcium** and **iron**, along with smaller amounts of
micronutrients.

PREPARATION: rye grains can be cooked like **rice**.
Crack them first using a rolling pin, in order to
allow them to absorb the water, and then boil in
salted water for an hour or more until tender.

USES: rye flour can be used to make a heavy,
dark **bread** (usually mixed with **wheat** flour). Rye
flakes may be added to savoury crumble toppings
or to **muesli** mixtures. Cooked rye grains can be
used in casseroles and bakes, to stuff vegetables or
as a side dish.

rye flour A **flour** ground from the cereal **rye**,
containing some **gluten**.

USES: rye flour can be used on its own to make a
very dense bread, but it is more often used with
wheat flour in baking.

safflower seed oil   A vegetable **oil** extracted from the safflower seed, which may be golden yellow or, if refined, colourless and odourless. It is high in **polyunsaturated fats** and is a rich source of linoleic acid. It is used for salad dressings and for frying.

saffron   The dried, yellow-orange stigmas of crocus flowers, used like a **spice**. To preserve its colour it should be stored in a dark glass jar.

USES: saffron is valued mainly for its colour and can be used to colour **rice** and other **cereals**, soups and casseroles. It is very expensive, however, and **turmeric** is an adequate alternative.

sage   The grey-green leaves of a perennial Mediterranean plant used fresh or dried, whole or powdered, as a **herb**. It should be stored in a sealed container to preserve its aroma.

USES: sage is perhaps best known as an ingredient of sage and **onion** stuffing. Vegetarians may enjoy home-made stuffing mixes baked separately in a bowl in the oven, or wrapped in puff pastry. Sage also goes well with **tomato** sauces, soups and **lentil** dishes.

sago   A grainy substance obtained from the pithy part of the trunk of the sago palm, which consists almost entirely of **starch** and no other nutrients. Sago should be stored in a sealed container and has a long shelf life.

USES: to make **milk** puddings.

sago flour A starchy, **gluten**-free **flour** obtained by grinding **sago** granules. It is available from some health-food shops or by mail-order from specialist outlets. Otherwise it can be ground at home using a coffee grinder.

USES: as a thickener in soups and casseroles, and also in baking, alone or mixed with other flours.

salsify (also called **oyster plant**) A tapering, white-skinned, **root vegetable**, which looks like a thin **parsnip**. Salsify has a delicate taste which has been likened to **asparagus** and to oysters. It has a high water content, with only small amounts of **protein**, **vitamins** and **minerals**. It contains no **starch** or **sugars**, but it does contain inulin, a complex sugar that has similar properties to **dietary fibre**. Salsify will stay fresh for one week in a plastic bag in the refrigerator.

PREPARATION: salsify should not be peeled until after it has been boiled in order to retain its full flavour. First trim and scrub, then cut into pieces and boil for 25 minutes in water with a little **lemon** juice. The skins will then come off easily. Alternatively, like many root vegetables, salsify can be baked, puréed or fried in batter.

USES: the flavour of salsify is best appreciated when it is served boiled with a little **butter** and chopped fresh **parsley**. It can also be used in casseroles, soups, or grated raw in salads.

salt (also called **common salt** or **table salt**) A white powder or crystalline solid consisting of sodium chloride and used for seasoning and preserving food. It is the main source of **sodium** in the diet. Salt occurs naturally in foods but it is also added during cooking, sometimes at the table, and also by food manufacturers. Foods that have high salt contents include **cheese**, canned vegetables, commercially prepared soups, sauces and breakfast cereals, **stock** cubes, **yeast extract** and savoury snack foods. See also **salt substitute**.

salt substitute A commercially prepared white powder that looks and tastes like **salt**, but which has a far lower **sodium** content and is, therefore, considered to be less harmful to the health. However, it is usually prepared from potassium chloride, which may not be suitable for people with certain medical conditions.

Santa Claus melon A variety of **melon**, so named because it may be stored, in the right conditions, until Christmas. It has green and yellow, rather rough skin and fragrant but watery flesh.

sapodilla (also called **naseberry**) A small, round, tropical **fruit** with rough, brown skin and soft, granular, beige flesh, which tastes like sweet **banana**. To tell when it is ripe, it should feel slightly soft and the skin should show no green when scratched. It can be stored at room temperature until ripe.

PREPARATION: chill, then peel and halve, removing the pips which have dangerous hooks. It can then be eaten raw.

USES: in a fruit salad or on its own with **cream**, or puréed and served in glasses, or as a flavouring for home-made ice cream.

satsuma   A small **citrus fruit** with characteristically loose, bright orange rind and sweet, juicy, orange flesh in crescent-shaped segments, virtually free of pips. Satsumas have a high water content, but they do offer some **carotene**, **vitamin C** and **folic acid**. They can be stored in the refrigerator or in a fruit bowl for up to a week.

PREPARATION: peel and separate the segments or slice across the centre.

USES: satsumas are easy to peel and a useful small fruit for lunches and snacks. They can also be used in fruit salads or as a garnish on cheesecakes and sponge cakes.

saturated fats   See **polyunsaturated fats**.

savory   The small, pointed leaves of an evergreen, Eurasian shrub, used fresh or dried, whole or powdered, as a **herb**. Store in a sealed container to preserve the flavour.

USES: traditionally, savory is used to flavour **lentil** soup and **broad beans**. It also goes well with **cheese** and **egg** dishes and can be used in salads.

savoy cabbage   A variety of **cabbage** with crisp, dark green, crumpled leaves. Like other cabbages savoy cabbage is a good source of **potassium, vitamin C** and **folic acid**. It stays fresh for one week wrapped in clingfilm and stored in the refrigerator.

PREPARATION: wash and shred the leaves, and boil for five minutes. Drain and serve with **butter** and **herbs**, or top with **cheese** and grill until browned. Savoy cabbage can also be braised or stir-fried.

USES: normally as a hot side vegetable, but for variety, serve with a sauce or **spices**, or use in casseroles, vegetable crumbles and soups.

scallion   See **spring onion**.

scarlet runner   See **runner bean**

scorzonera   A black rooted variety of **salsify**.

Scotch barley   See **pot barley**.

Scotch kale   See **curly kale**.

seakale beet   See **Swiss chard**.

sea vegetable   An alternative name for **seaweed**.

seaweed (also called **sea vegetable**) Marine plants or algae that are cultivated or harvested from the wild and eaten as vegetables or powdered and sprinkled on food. Seaweeds are one of the few reliable sources of **iodine**, but they also have a high **sodium** content. See **arame**; **dulse**; **hiziki**; **kelp**; **kombu**; **laver**; **nori**; **wakame**.

seed The mature, fertilized 'egg' of a plant that usually contains the fertile germ, surrounded by a store of nutrients and a tough outer skin. The nutritional properties of seeds vary according to the species, but in general they provide **protein**, **polyunsaturated fats**, some **dietary fibre**, **sugars** and **starch** as well as some **vitamins** and **minerals**. See **linseeds**; **poppy seed**; **pumpkin seed**; **sesame seed**; **sunflower seed**. See also **nasturtium**; **sprouted seeds**.

seitan (also called **zeitan**) A commercially manufactured **meat substitute** made from **wheat** gluten, which very closely imitates the texture and taste of meat. Seitan is not yet commercially available as an ingredient in the UK, but it is used by manufacturers to produce ready-prepared vegetarian sausages and **burgers**.

selenium A **trace element** involved in the body's defence mechanisms. Together with **vitamin E** it is part of the antioxidant system responsible for preserving the structure and function of all membranes. The major source of selenium in a vegetarian diet is **cereals**, especially **bread**, but **cheese**, **eggs**, **walnuts** and **brazil nuts** are also good sources. The selenium content of plants depends upon the amount of selenium in the soil where they are grown, and deficiencies have only been reported in areas with poor soil selenium levels, such as parts of China and New Zealand.

semi-skimmed milk Homogenized pasteurized **milk** that contains only half the fat content (1.5 to 1.8%) of whole milk. It is lower in saturated fats (see **polyunsaturated fats**) and in Calories than whole milk.

semolina A grainy powder derived from the inner endosperm of hard or **durum wheat**, which is high in **gluten**. Semolina is used commercially to make **pasta** and is sold as a powder. It is high in **starch** and contains some **protein**, but it does not contain significant amounts of **micronutrients**.

USES: to make **milk** puddings and also in some sweet desserts, cakes and cheesecake.

sesame salt See **gomasio**.

sesame seed The tiny, oily, golden seed of a tropical herbaceous plant of East Indian origin. Sesame seeds are rich in **polyunsaturated fats** and the oil is extracted to make **sesame seed oil**. The seeds provide some **protein**, but their **iron, calcium** and **magnesium** content is largely unavailable because of the presence of **phytic acid**. Sesame seeds should be stored in an airtight container and have a long shelf life.

USES: add to breads or biscuits, or use for decoration, sprinkle onto salads, stir-fries and cooked vegetables, use in sweet or savoury crumble toppings. Sesame seeds are used commercially to make **tahini**, and also to make **halva**, a Middle-Eastern sweet.

sesame seed oil The dark, strong-flavoured vegetable **oil** extracted from the **sesame seed**. It is high in **polyunsaturated fats**, including linoleic acid, and also contains some **vitamin E**.

Seville orange A variety of **orange** with a bitter flavour and, therefore, rarely eaten raw. They are most commonly used to make marmalade.

shaddock See **pomelo**.

shallot A small bulb related to the **onion**, with a sweet, intense taste that is less pungent than an onion. Shallots have a high water content and only small amounts of **micronutrients**. They can be stored in a cool dry place for up to one month.
PREPARATION: shallots may be used in the same way as onions, but in frying they must not be allowed to brown as this makes them taste bitter.
USES: as you would onions, especially in sauces, casseroles and soups, or raw in salads.

sharon fruit A **fruit** that is closely related to the **persimmon**, with orange, edible skin, edible seeds and a sweet taste (similar to a combination of melon and peach). Sharon fruit can be stored in the refrigerator for a few days.

PREPARATION: wash and eat raw, either whole or sliced into segments.

USES: as part of a fruit salad, perhaps with peaches, melon and grapes, or use thin slices as a garnish.

sheeps' milk   See **ewes' milk**.

shitake or **shiitake mushroom**   A small, wild **mushroom** with a white stem and purplish-brown cap, which is a member of the boletus family native to Japan. The stem is rather tough, but may be used to flavour a dish and removed before serving. Shitake mushrooms are available fresh and dried, and are most commonly used in Japanese dishes although they can be used wherever mushrooms are required.

short-grain rice   Any of a variety of types of **rice** that have relatively short, plump grains, which tend to clump together on cooking. See **pudding rice**; **glutinous rice**.

shoyu   A variety of **soya sauce**.

silken tofu   A variety of **tofu** that is not pressed as heavily as **firm tofu** and has a soft texture.

PREPARATION: it does not hold its shape well and is best used puréed in sweet **fruit** dishes or used to make a **vegan** sauce.

USES: to make vegan cheesecakes, creamy **yoghurt** desserts and **egg-free mayonnaise**.

skimmed milk   A type of **milk** that has been skimmed to remove virtually all the **fat**. Skimmed milk is very low in saturated fats (see **polyunsaturated fats**) and also low in Calories so it is regarded as healthier than whole milk. However, it lacks the fat-soluble **vitamins** found in whole milk. Skimmed milk should not be given to babies and small children under the age of five years for whom milk forms a major part of the diet.

slimming   A vegetarian diet is not automatically a slimming diet, and some people find that they gain weight if they rely on **cheese** or **nuts** to take the place of meat on their plates. It is quite possible to remain vegetarian on a slimming diet, by reducing the intake of sugary and fatty foods and increasing the amount of nutritious low-Calorie fruits and vegetables.

sloe   The small, sour, blue-black **fruit** of the blackthorn. Sloes are not available commercially, but they can be harvested from the wild in October and November, after the first frost. They are rich in **vitamin C** but have a very sour taste. They can be stored in the refrigerator for a day or two.

PREPARATION: like all **wild foods** sloes must be washed thoroughly before use.

USES: mainly to make sloe gin, by steeping the washed and pricked berries in gin for around 10 weeks. They can also be used in jam and wine making.

smetana or **smatana**   A type of **soured cream** made from **skimmed milk** and **cream**, fermented in the presence of bacteria in a similar way to **yoghurt**. Although it has less **fat** than soured cream it is not low in fat. Depending on the milk and cream used, smetana can be high in saturated fats (see **polyunsaturated fats**), but because of the bacterial activity it is easier to digest than milk or cream. It can be stored in the refrigerator for up to a week.

PREPARATION: to make smetana at home, heat half a pint of skimmed milk and half a pint of single cream together in a saucepan to around 43-44°C/110-115°F. Thoroughly mix in two tablespoons of commercially prepared smetana. Pour the mixture into a thermos flask and incubate for 12 hours.

USES: as an alternative to cream or yoghurt in recipes and as a topping for fresh-fruit or sweet desserts, such as sponge cake or cheesecake.

smoked tofu   A variety of **firm tofu** that is sold ready smoked and vacuum-packed. It has a distinctive smoky flavour, which is quite similar to that of smoked meat. Smoked tofu is best used sliced and fried with rice or in stir-fries or kebabs, or it can be puréed for a smoky dip.

snow pea See **mangetout**.

sodium An essential **mineral** found chiefly in the blood and the fluids that surround cells. The remainder is held inside cells and as part of the structure of bones. Together with **potassium**, sodium is a major factor in maintaining the balance of body fluid. It helps regulate the levels of acidity and alkalinity in the body, and it contributes to the functioning of muscles and nerves. It also stimulates the excretion of unwanted substances by the kidneys and therefore decreases the risk of kidney stones. The most common form of sodium is common **salt** (sodium chloride).

Because salt is so readily available – it occurs naturally in many foods, is added by manufacturers, or at home during cooking and at the table – deficiency is very rare except after severe diarrhoea or excessive sweating. High sodium intakes are far more common and have been linked with an increased susceptibility to hypertension.

soft cheese Any of a wide variety of **cheeses** that are not completely hardened, but are soft enough to spread. The fact that a cheese is soft does not necessarily mean that it is free from **animal rennet**.

soluble fibre See **dietary fibre**.

sorghum A large grain related to **millet**, which is a staple food in parts of Africa. It is not widely available in Britain but can sometimes be purchased from wholefood shops.

PREPARATION: the whole grains can be cooked as you would **rice** in boiling water for around an hour and will retain a chewy texture. Alternatively, whole grains can be ground at home to a flour that can be mixed with wheat **flour** in breadmaking. Sorghum does not contain **gluten** and so it is suitable for those who must keep to a gluten-free diet.

USES: as for rice and as an accompaniment to a casserole.

sorghum flour A **gluten**-free **flour**, which can be ground from the cereal **sorghum**. It is available from some health-food shops or by mail-order from specialist outlets.

USES: to make gluten-free baked goods.

sorrel A perennial leaf vegetable with a sharp taste. It is popular in French cuisine but little used in the UK. Sorrel does not store well, but it can be kept in the refrigerator for a day or two.

PREPARATION: wash the leaves and then cook them in the water that clings to them, as you would spinach. Alternatively, finely chopped, raw leaves can be added to salads.

USES: in soups, sauces and omelettes, and in salads.

sour or **soured cream** A type of single **cream** that has developed a sour taste after the addition of bacteria similar to those used to make **yoghurt**. Sour cream has the same **fat** content as single cream (18%) and is high in saturated fats (see **polyunsaturated fats**), but due to the bacterial activity it is easier to digest. It must be stored, covered, in the refrigerator.

USES: in some tart sauces and dips, and as a contrast to sweet fruit or cake desserts.

soursop A variety of **custard apple**, which is very large – up to one foot long and 4.54 kg (10lbs) in weight – with thin, green skin covered in rows of spines. The flesh has a more tart and refreshing flavour than that of the other fruits in the family.

soya bean The highly nutritious, white-fleshed seed of an Asian bean plant; a **pulse**. The soya bean provides **protein**, **fat**, mostly as **polyunsaturated fats**, **starch** and **dietary fibre**. It is a good source of well-absorbed **iron**, which makes it a valuable part of vegetarian and **vegan** diets. Soya beans also contain **manganese**, **molybdenum**, **riboflavin**, **vitamin B$_6$**, **vitamin E** and **vitamin K**. It is one of the best plant sources of protein and is used as a **meat substitute** all over the world. It is also added to many manufactured foods, such as sausages and beef burgers, as a meat extender and to increase their protein content.

PREPARATION: soya beans are the most difficult of beans to cook at home. They must be soaked overnight, then rinsed thoroughly and boiled for 10 minutes to destroy toxic **lectins**. They are then simmered until tender. This can take between one and three hours, and may take as long as eight hours. Putting the beans in a pressure cooker after boiling can help reduce the cooking time. Once cooked, soya beans can be used whole or mashed. Soya beans can also be soaked and allowed to produce crisp white **bean sprouts**. This process also destroys toxic lectins.

USES: cooked soya beans can be added to soups and casseroles, mashed to make bakes and **burgers** or a paté, or used to make **soya milk**. See also **tempeh**.

soya bean curd   See **tofu**.

soya cheese   A commercially prepared **cheese** substitute made from **soya beans** and suitable for a **vegan** diet. Although it does not really taste like cheese it is a useful food and progress is being made towards the production of a good vegan hard cheese.

soya cream   A **vegan** cream substitute made from concentrated **soya milk**.

soya fibre See **okara**.

soya flour A nutritious **flour** made from ground soya beans. Soya flour can be used like a food supplement to add to the **protein** content of **bread**, soups and sauces. It can also be mixed with water to use as a substitute for **eggs** to bind ingredients.

soya ice cream A **vegan** ice cream made from soya milk. There are a number of different commercial brands and flavours available.

soya milk A **vegan** milk substitute made from soya beans, which is rich in **protein**, low in **fat** and sometimes contains added vitamins including **vitamin B$_{12}$** and raw sugar as a sweetener. Organic (see **organic foods**) and flavoured soya milks are also available. Soya milk has become more palatable in recent years, but its taste is not at all similar to cows' **milk**.

PREPARATION: soya milk can be prepared at home. The soya beans are soaked overnight, then rinsed and puréed. The purée is mixed with water and boiled thoroughly to destroy toxic **lectins**. The liquid is then strained to yield soya milk and a fibrous residue called **okara**.

USES: although soya milk can be used in almost the same way as cows' milk it has a tendency to curdle in hot drinks and to separate in baked sauces. It can also be used to make **tofu** and **soya yoghurt**.

soya oil The vegetable **oil** extracted from the **soya bean**. Soya oil contains a high proportion of **polyunsaturated fats**, including linoleic acid, and is a good source of **vitamin E**. It can be used in cooking and is used commercially to make margarines high in polyunsaturated fats.

soya sauce (also called **soy sauce**) A spicy, dark, savoury, Japanese sauce made from fermented **soya beans**, with added wheat and salt. Traditional tamari and shoyu sauces are fermented for at least 18 months. Cheaper versions of soya sauce are likely to contain artificial colouring and **monosodium glutamate**. Soya sauce is high in **protein** and although it is used in small amounts it is said to be beneficial to the digestion.

USES: in all kinds of savoury dishes including casseroles, soups, sauces, stir-fries and fried **tofu** and vegetables. Add a dash to dry roasting sunflower and pumpkins seeds or use in a marinade or salad dressing.

soya yoghurt A variety of **yoghurt** made from **soya milk**. It is commercially produced in a number of different flavours and can also be made at home in the same way as ordinary yoghurt.

spaghetti A variety of **pasta** shaped in to very long thin strands. Spaghetti is available white (made with refined **flour**) or brown (made with wholemeal flour) and is commonly served with a

tomato or bolognaise sauce. A vegetarian bolognaise sauce can be made by substituting the minced meat with **textured vegetable protein** mince.

spaghetti squash A variety of **winter squash** with bland-tasting flesh that forms long strands, which look, and can be served like, white spaghetti.

Spanish onion A large variety of **onion** with a mild flavour which can be used raw in salads.

spearmint A variety of **mint**, which is used as a **herb**.

spelt A variety of **wheat**, once extensively cultivated and which was used to develop present-day cultivated wheats.

spice Any of a variety of seeds, stems or roots of certain aromatic plants that are used whole or ground to add flavour to food. See **allspice**; **amchoor**; **aniseed**; **asafoetida**; **black onion seed**; **black pepper**; **caraway seed**; **cardamom**; **cayenne pepper**; **chilli powder**; **Chinese five spice**; **cinnamon**; **clove**; **cumin**; **curry powder**; **garam marsala**; **ginger**; **mace**; **mixed spice**; **nutmeg**; **paprika**; **saffron**; **turmeric**.

spinach A leafy green **vegetable**. Spinach is a good source of **dietary fibre** and contains more

protein than other vegetables. It is high in **carotene** and contains some **riboflavin**, **vitamin C** and **vitamin E**. Although spinach has a high **iron** and **calcium** content, the iron is poorly absorbed and the presence of **oxalic acid** prevents the absorption of calcium.

Spinach is available fresh, according to the season, frozen, as whole or shredded leaves, and canned. It is best used on the day of purchase as the leaves quickly become limp and the flavour deteriorates. If necessary, store for not more than two days in a plastic bag in the refrigerator.

PREPARATION: wash the leaves thoroughly, trim the ends of the stalks and tear out any particularly tough midribs. Place the leaves in a pan with the water that adheres to them and cook for five to ten minutes. There will be a substantial reduction in bulk.

USES: serve as a hot side vegetable with **butter** and **nutmeg**, or use in an omelette, soup, or as a base for poached **eggs**.

spinach beet (also called **perpetual spinach**) A perennial plant that is related to **beetroot** (not to **spinach**), whose leaves can be used in the same way as spinach. The flavour is stronger and the leaves are darker and fleshier. Like spinach, spinach beet does not store well but if necessary can be kept in the refrigerator for up to two days.

PREPARATION: wash the leaves thoroughly and trim the bases of the stems. Place in a pan with the water that adheres to them and cook for five to ten minutes, as you would spinach.

USES: in any recipe that uses spinach, or as a hot side vegetable.

spirits Distilled alcoholic liquors. Spirits are concentrated sources of **alcohol** with variable levels of **sugar**. A few are unsuitable for vegetarians, for example Campari contains **cochineal**, and one brand of tequila is sold in a bottle containing a worm.

spirulina A minute alga found in freshwater and alkaline lakes. Spirulina is almost self-supporting, taking energy from sunlight, carbon dioxide from the air and minerals from the water. It contains small amounts of **protein**, **minerals** and **vitamins**, and is one of the few plant sources of **vitamin B$_{12}$**. It is, therefore, a useful supplement for **vegans** and is available as tablets.

split lentil A **puy lentil** that has been split in half and has had its outer skin removed to reveal the small orange discs which are commonly thought of as **lentils**. Split lentils have a similar nutritional value to puy lentils and a long shelf life.

PREPARATION: split lentils do not need to be soaked before they are cooked, but they should be sorted carefully and any small stones removed. Bring to the boil, then allow to boil for 10 minutes and then simmer for 20-30 minutes. Split lentils lose their shape easily and may reduce to a lumpy, floury paste. It is important to use an appropriate amount of water, depending on the use for which they are intended, as cooked split lentils can be watery.

USES: split lentils make an excellent warming soup, or add Indian spices to make a hot **dhal** in which to dip Indian **bread**. They can also be used to make a cold sandwich spread, or used in **burgers** and bakes.

split pea   A dried pea that has been split in half and has had its beige, outer skin removed to yield a large, yellow or green split pea. Split peas are a good source of **protein**, as well as of **dietary fibre**. They also contain **potassium**, **calcium**, **magnesium**, **manganese**, **carotene** and **folic acid**.

PREPARATION: they do not need to be soaked and can be boiled for 10 minutes and then simmered for 45 to 60 minutes. However, soaking overnight will reduce the cooking time to 25 to 30 minutes. Like **split lentils**, split peas lose their shape easily and may reduce to a lumpy floury paste. It is important to use the right amount of water, depending on the use for which they are intended, as cooked split peas can be watery.

USES: they can be used in similar ways to split lentils.

spring greens   See **greens**.

spring onion (also called **scallion**) A tiny immature **onion**, with a slightly higher nutritional profile than fully grown onions, but which are used in
far smaller quantities. They can be stored in the
refrigerator for up to one week.

PREPARATION: top and tail, and wash thoroughly. Spring onions are generally used raw.

USES: in salads or with dips or a fondue, or use in
a stir-fry.

sprouted seeds Many **seeds** and whole **cereals**
can be soaked overnight in water and then kept in
moist conditions and allowed to form crisp
sprouts, in exactly the same way as **beans** are
allowed to form **bean sprouts**. Sprouted seeds and
grains are very nutritious and can be used in sandwiches, stir-fries and salads.

squash Any of a variety of large fruits, with a
hard rind and pulpy flesh, which is treated as a
vegetable. Squashes have a high water content and
contain a small amount of **protein**, some **dietary
fibre** and some **carotene**. See **acorn squash**; **butternut squash**; **chayote**; **courgette**; **hubbard squash**;
marrow; **pattypan squash**; **pumpkin**; **spaghetti
squash**; **turban squash**; **yellow squash**. See also
summer squash; **winter squash**.

star apple See **star fruit**.

starch A polysaccharide made up of long chains
of **glucose** molecules. It is used as an energy store

in most plants. Starch is broken down during digestion by **enzymes** into **glucose**, which is then absorbed into the bloodstream; uncooked starch is poorly digested. It is found in greatest quantities in **bananas**, **bread**, biscuits, **cassava**, **corn**, **flour**, **oats**, **pearl barley**, **potatoes**, **semolina**, **sago**, **tapioca** and **yams**. See also **carbohydrate**.

star fruit (also called **carambola** or **star apple**) An attractive, yellow tropical **fruit**, with waxy, translucent skin, which in cross section is shaped like a five-pointed star. It has a high water content and offers little **protein** or **micronutrients** although it does contain some **vitamin C**. It can be stored in the refrigerator for up to a week, depending on freshness.

PREPARATION: wash and slice thinly across the centre. Remove the pips and use the flesh raw.

USES: star fruit is valued mainly for its decorative shape although it also has a pleasant flavour. It is commonly used as a garnish and in salads and fruit salads.

steaming A method of cooking by suspending the food over boiling water. Steaming has the advantage over **boiling** that fewer **micronutrients** are **leached** out during the cooking process. Only **vitamins** that are unstable at high temperatures (e.g. **pantothenic acid**, **thiamin** and **vitamin C**) will be depleted by steaming. A wide variety of **vegetables** can be steamed, such as **potatoes**, **carrots**,

broccoli and **cauliflower**. Steaming is a good way of reheating cooked vegetables. **Couscous**, a grain-like dish made from wheat semolina, can also be prepared by steaming.

sterilized milk Whole, **homogenized milk** that is bottled and then subjected to heat treatment of at least 100°C for between 20 and 30 minutes. This gives it a longer shelf life than normal milk but causes a 35% reduction of the **thiamin** content and 50% of the **vitamin B$_{12}$** content.

stewing A method of cooking food in water or stock so that the temperature does not rise above simmering point (90°C). Stewed foods retain most of their **vitamins** and **minerals**, because they are served with the juices, and because stewing involves moderate temperatures that do not destroy those vitamins that are susceptible to heat (**pantothenic acid**, **thiamin** and **vitamin C**). Many **fruits**, such as **apples**, **gooseberries**, **rhubarb** and **tomatoes**, can be served stewed.

sticky rice See **glutinous rice**.

stir-fry A method of cooking that originated in the Far East, in which foods are first cut into small regular pieces and are then quickly fried in a rounded pan or wok. Small quantities of **sesame** or **sunflower oil** are used. The food is cooked only briefly at a very high temperature. This method of cooking lends itself particularly well to the preparation of **vegetables**, which retain their crispness and most of their **vitamin** content. Only vitamins that are unstable at high temperatures (e.g. **pantothenic acid**, **thiamin** and **vitamin C**) are depleted by stir-frying. Vegetables that might be included in a stir-fried dish include **bean sprouts**, red and green **peppers**, **spring onions**, **mushrooms**, **courgettes**, **carrots** and **tomatoes**. During cooking, stir-fried foods are commonly seasoned with **soy sauce** and once cooked served with **rice** or **noodles**.

stock   Vegetarian stock can be made from the water left after vegetables have been boiled, or by adding water to a vegetable stock cube, powder or paste. Vegetable stock cubes may contain food **additives**, such as **monosodium glutamate**, and have a high **salt** content.

strained yoghurt   See **Greek yoghurt**.

strawberry   The sweet, fleshy, red **fruit** of the strawberry plant. Fresh strawberries are mainly available in the summer although imported strawberries begin to be available earlier in the year. They can be purchased fresh or canned, or harvested at farms where you can pick your own fruit. They are a very popular fruit with a taste that is sometimes insipid but at its best is very sweet. They contain **sugars** and some **dietary fibre**, with small amounts of **pantothenic acid**, and a good amount of **vitamin C**. They do not store well and are best used on the day of purchase.

PREPARATION: rinse and hull, and use raw.

USES: on their own, with cream, or in a fruit salad, or as a garnish. They can also be used to make a fruity sauce, to flavour home-made ice cream and in jam making. See also **alpine strawberry**.

strawberry tomato (also called **ground cherry**) A **fruit** closely related to the **cape gooseberry**, but with a smaller, sweeter berry and a thinner husk. Strawberry tomatoes can be used in the same way as cape gooseberries, but they are not widely available.

straw mushroom A variety of small **mushroom** native to China, which is traditionally cultivated on a bed of straw. They are at their best when very young before the cap has separated from the stem to reveal the gills. They do not store well and should be kept in a plastic bag in the refrigerator for not more than two days.

PREPARATION: wash thoroughly and trim the bottom of the stalk; peeling is not necessary.

USES: in speciality Chinese-style dishes or as an alternative to button mushrooms in any recipe.

string bean See **French bean**.

sucrose (common name **sugar**) A **carbohydrate**, or disaccharide of **glucose** and **fructose**. Sucrose occurs naturally in beet and cane sugar, from which it is commercially refined, and in smaller amounts in fruit and some root vegetables. It is available in many forms in various stages of refinement: white sugars (e.g. caster, granulated and icing sugar) are the most refined; brown sugars (e.g. demerara and muscovado) are less refined; sugars that are described as raw (e.g. raw cane sugar) are the least refined. Sugar is consumed in foods such as preserves, cordials, confectionery, cakes and biscuits. It is used commercially as a sweetener and as a preservative.

Sucrose is broken down by **enzymes** in the digestive tract to its constituent monosaccharides, glucose and fructose, which are absorbed and carried in the blood to the liver and used for energy supply. Sucrose is virtually 100% carbohydrate with no other nutritional value. It encourages the growth of bacteria that cause dental decay and may cause yeasts in the body to multiply so rapidly that yeast infections develop. The diet of many people would benefit from a reduction of sugar consumption.

suet A solid, white **fat** obtained from the body fat of animals, including cows and sheep. Suet is not suitable for vegetarians and they should be aware that it is often used as an ingredient in puddings and **mincemeat**. A type of suet suitable for vegetarians, made from **vegetable fat**, is available from health-food shops and many supermarkets.

sugar See **sucrose**.

sugar apple (also called **sweetsop**) A variety of **custard apple** covered in large, yellow-green scales and with sweet-tasting, banana-flavoured flesh.

sugar pea See **mangetout**.

sugars Simple **carbohydrates** (monosaccharides and disaccharides) present in food, including **sucrose**, **glucose**, **fructose**, **maltose** and **lactose**. They are all sweet-tasting and have the same energy value of 394 kcal/100 g. Many vegetarians, who have chosen the diet for health reasons, are aware that sugars contribute significantly to tooth decay and are a poor source of carbohydrates because they offer no other nutrients. For this reason they may aim to obtain their energy requirements from complex carbohydrates and they may also prefer to use unrefined sugars, **concentrated fruit juices**, or **honey** to sweeten their food where necessary.

sulphur A non-metallic **mineral** that, along with **potassium**, is the third most common mineral in the body (after **calcium** and **phosphorus**). It is present in the essential amino acids methionine and is a component of **biotin** and **thiamin**. These substances cannot be synthesized by the body, so they must be supplied by the diet. Good sources of sulphur include **mustard** powder, **nuts**, **garlic** and

cheese. In order to ensure a good intake of the essential amino acids that contain sulphur, the diet should contain **protein** from a variety of sources. The amino acids and **vitamins** that contain sulphur are responsible for maintaining healthy hair, nails and skin, for promoting mental activity and the secretion of bile.

sultana A dried white **grape** (a dried black grape is called a **raisin**). Sultanas are a rich source of **sugars**, with some **dietary fibre**, **potassium**, **iron**, and small amounts of other vitamins and minerals. They should be stored in a sealed container in a cool, dry place, and have a long shelf life.

PREPARATION: wash before use as some dried fruits are coated with mineral oil to improve their appearance and prevent them from clumping together.

USES: sultanas make a nutritious snack and can be added to muesli or sprinkled into salads and used in cakes. Soaked in **lemon** juice they are a delicious addition to a plain cheesecake, and they can also add unexpected sweetness to curry sauces.

summer squash The term used to describe varieties of **squash** (including **courgettes**) which have thin skins and are more perishable than hard-skinned **winter squashes**. Summer squashes are often less watery than winter squashes. See **chayote**; **pattypan squash**; **yellow squash**.

243

sunberry   A variety of hybrid berry, which looks like an elongated **raspberry** with a sharp taste similar to a **loganberry**. It is best used for cooking rather than for eating raw and is not grown commercially except on some pick-your-own farms.

sunflower oil   The vegetable **oil** extracted from **sunflower seeds**. Sunflower oil is high in **polyunsaturated fats**, including linoleic acid, and is a good source of **vitamin E**. It is used for frying and for salad dressings.

sunflower seed   The small, highly nutritious seeds of the sunflower, with tough, black and white striped shells and a smooth, oily, stone-coloured, pleasantly-flavoured kernel. Sunflower seeds provide an exceptionally good source of **protein** (for a plant source) and have a high **polyunsaturated fat** content, including a high percentage of linoleic acid. They are a good source of **vitamin E** and provide **vitamin A**, **B complex vitamins**, **vitamin D**, **iron**, **potassium**, **phosphorus**, **magnesium**, **manganese**, **copper** and **calcium**. Because of their high fat content they should be purchased in small quantities and stored in a sealed container.

PREPARATION: most sunflower seeds are sold shelled, but you may find them unshelled. Removing the shells is a tricky job. Do not eat sunflower seeds sold as plant seed or pet food as these may have been treated with chemicals unsuitable for human consumption. Sunflower seeds can be roasted in a dry frying pan, perhaps with a dash of **soya sauce**, or ground and used in baking.

USES: as a nutritious snack food or cocktail nibble, or sprinkled onto muesli or salads, or in crumble toppings and bread.

surinam cherry See **pitagna**.

swede
(also called **rutabaga**) A bulbous, Eurasian **root vegetable** related to the **turnip**, with pulpy, orange flesh. Swedes have a high water content and offer some **sugars** with only small amounts of **dietary fibre** (including **pectin**), **B complex vitamins** and **vitamin C**. Swedes can be kept in a cool dry place for up to five days.

PREPARATION: peel until the yellow flesh is exposed and cut off the root and top. Cut into small pieces and boil until tender. Swedes can also be roasted in pieces like **parsnips**.

USES: traditionally, swede is served mashed as a hot side vegetable, although it is quite watery. It can be improved by mashing with boiled potatoes or by adding **butter** and **pepper**, or **ginger** or **nutmeg**. Swedes can also be used in casseroles and soups.

sweet chestnut See **chestnut**.

sweetcorn
The tender, sweet-tasting yellow kernels of unripe **maize**. Sweetcorn is available

fresh on the cob (in which case it needs to be boiled before it is eaten) or pre-cooked and canned. Fresh sweetcorn contains **starch**, some **protein** and **dietary fibre**, a small amount of **sugars** and some **magnesium**, **molybdenum**, **phosphorus**, **thiamin**, **niacin** and **vitamin E**. Corn on the cob should have plump kernels and if sold in the husk should look green and fresh. It should be used as soon as possible after purchase although it can be refrigerated in the husk for one or two days.

PREPARATION: place the cobs in boiling water for between five and eight minutes until the kernels can be easily stripped from the cob with a fork. Be careful not to over-cook because the skins will toughen.

USES: fresh sweetcorn can be served 'on the cob'. Alternatively, it can be stripped from the cob and served with melted **butter** and seasoning. The kernels can also be used in soups and casseroles or in salads, or as a pizza topping.

sweetie A large **citrus fruit** that looks like an unripe grapefruit, with thick, green skin and yellow, juicy, segmented flesh. It has been especially bred to be sweet, not tart, and has no pips.

PREPARATION: either peel and separate the segments or cut into eight segments and eat the flesh off the rind, or halve and serve as you would a grapefruit.

USES: in a fruit salad or for breakfast, or squeeze for fruit juice.

sweet lime   See **limetta**.

sweet marjoram   See **marjoram**.

sweet pepper   See **pepper**.

sweet potato   A starchy tuber from a plant related to the bindweed family, native to North America. A sweet potato is not the same as a **yam**. Sweet potatoes are smaller with a smoother, pinkish skin. They contain **starch**, **sugars**, some **dietary fibre** and a little **protein**, with **potassium**, **phosphorus**, **carotene**, **thiamin**, **niacin** and **vitamin E** and small amounts of **vitamins A** and **C**. They can be stored at a cool room temperature for approximately one week.

PREPARATION: scrub the skins and then place the sweet potatoes in boiling water and boil until tender. Remove the skins and mash with **milk**, **butter**, **salt** and **pepper**. Alternatively, wrap the scrubbed sweet potatoes in foil and bake as you would a potato.

USES: as a hot side vegetable or in a casserole or soup.

sweet rice   See **glutinous rice**.

sweetsop   See **sugar apple**.

Swiss chard (also called **chard**, **leaf beet** or **seakale beet**)   A leaf vegetable of the beet family which is used like **spinach** although it has thicker stalks and a milder flavour. Fresh Swiss chard is rich in **vitamin C**. The leaves should be quite crisp and are best used immediately, though they can be stored in a plastic bag in the refrigerator for one or two days.

PREPARATION: wash the leaves thoroughly in cold water, then strip them away from the midribs and cook them with the water that remains on them from washing for five to ten minutes. Lightly boil or steam whole stalks and midribs for about 20 minutes (as you would **asparagus**), alternatively, chop into pieces and boil for 15 minutes.

USES: as a hot side vegetable or as a mild-flavoured substitute for spinach in recipes. The stalks can be served with a sauce, or used raw in a salad or dip.

tabasco A thin, red sauce with a very strong, peppery flavour made from **vinegar**, red **chilli** pepper and **salt**.

USES: use sparingly to give flavour to casseroles, soups, stir-fries and sauces.

table salt See **salt**.

tagliatelle A variety of **pasta**, usually made with **egg**, shaped into thin ribbons and normally sold dried in bundles or coils. It is available white, brown (made with wholemeal **flour**) or green (coloured with **spinach**) and goes well with thick, creamy pasta sauces.

tahini A smooth, oily paste made from crushed **sesame seeds**, which has a strong, nutty flavour. Dark tahini is made from the seeds still with their husks and has a grainy texture with a more bitter flavour than light tahini, which is made from husked seeds.

Tahini is high in **polyunsaturated fats**, including linoleic acid. It is sold in jars and has a long shelf life if stored in a cool place.

USES: tahini is an essential ingredient of **hummus**, a Middle-Eastern dish made from **chickpeas**, and is also traditionally served with **falafel** balls, another Middle-Eastern vegetarian delicacy. Tahini may also be used as a dip or added to a salad dressing or sauce.

tamari A variety of **soya sauce** that is especially strong and dark.

tamarillo (also called **tree tomato** or **Java plum**) A large, oval **fruit** with inedible, orange-red skin and acidic flesh with many edible pips. It can be eaten as a vegetable with similar uses to a **tomato**.

PREPARATION: peel off the skin and stew, bake or grill. Alternatively, if the fruit is slightly soft and ripe, cut in half and eat the flesh with a spoon.

USES: as part of a fruit salad or as a hot side vegetable.

tamarind (also called **Indian date**) The fleshy pod of a tropical Indian plant with an extremely sour taste. Tamarind is sold at specialist Indian shops either as cakes of peeled and pressed pulp, or as a paste made by removing the fibrous pulp from the flesh.

PREPARATION: tamarind paste can be made at home from tamarind pulp. Soak a cake of pulp overnight in a bowl of boiling water, mash thoroughly to extract as much juice as possible, then strain to remove the pulp. The juice can be stored for a week in a jar in the refrigerator or frozen in an ice-cube tray and used as required.

USES: tamarind gives a tart taste to food and is used in many Indian dishes.

tangelo A cross between a **grapefruit** and a **tangerine**. See **ugli fruit**.

tangerine A small **citrus fruit** with bright orange skin and sweet, orange flesh in crescent-shaped segments with very few pips. Tangerines are rich in **vitamin C** and also offer some **sugars** and **dietary fibre**.

PREPARATION: peel off the skin and eat the segments raw.

USES: in a fruit salad or as a snack, or as a garnish. Tangerines can also be used to make marmalade.

tapioca A grainy **starch** obtained from the root of the **cassava** plant, available as pellets, flakes or flour. It is used commercially as a thickening agent and domestically as an ingredient of a **milk** pudding. It is 96% starch and is high in **Calories** but low in nutrients.

USES: bake with milk to make a hot milk pudding.

tapioca flour A fine, **gluten**-free **flour** derived from the **cassava** root. It is similar to **cassava flour** only more starchy.

taramasalata A creamy, pale pink paste, which is not suitable for vegetarians because it is made from fish roe.

taro (also called **eddoe** or **kandalla**) A thick-skinned, starchy tuber with dense flesh, rather drier than that of a **potato**, and with a distinctive nutty flavour.

PREPARATION: taro must be cooked thoroughly before eating as it contains poisonous substances. It can be cooked exactly as a potato (i.e. baked, boiled, roasted, fried, etc.) but the skin is inedible, and the roots may need to be boiled for longer than potatoes before they become tender.

USES: as a hot side vegetable. Taros can also be stuffed, perhaps with a **bean** and **mushroom** mixture, and baked. In Hawaii a strong alcoholic drink called *poi* is made from mashed and fermented taro tubers.

tarragon The small, toothed leaves of an aromatic, perennial plant that are used fresh or dried, chopped or powdered as a **herb**. Tarragon is considered by some to be helpful to the digestion.

USES: it is often used with fish and chicken, but vegetarians may enjoy its flavour with cheese and egg dishes, or chopped into a salad.

tayberry   A large, sweet, red **fruit** with a delicate flavour, which is a cross between a **raspberry**, a **blackberry** and a **loganberry**. The nutritional content is similar to that of a raspberry. Tayberries are rarely commercially available except from farms where you may pick your own fruit. They should be stored in the refrigerator for one or two days only.

PREPARATION: do not wash until you plan to use them, and do not wash at all if possible as this can impair the flavour. Pull out the white cores as gently as possible to avoid crushing the fruit.

USES: as part of a fruit salad or with a plain cheesecake, or in meringue nests with a little cream. Tayberries can also be used in jam and wine making.

tea   An infusion of dried, shredded leaves of one or several tea shrubs. Indian, Sri Lankan and Kenyan teas are strong and dark, and China tea is weaker and more aromatic. Tea can be served hot or cold, with or without **lemon** or **milk** and with or without **sugar**. It has no **Calories** but contains **caffeine** and theophylline (another strong stimulant), and also tannins which can interfere with the absorption of **iron** if drunk with a meal. Some teas are flavoured with fruits or flowers but they still have comparable levels of caffeine, theophylline and tannins.

Herbal teas and true infusions of fruits and flowers do not contain these substances. Many people prefer them as a healthier alternative and also for the medicinal properties that are attributed to them.

USES: as a hot or cold beverage or, cold, as an ingredient in some rich fruit cakes.

tempeh A fermented **soya bean** product used like a **meat substitute**. Soaked, hulled, boiled and mashed soya beans are pressed into a firm block with the addition of a bacterial culture. The resulting fermentation produces a savoury flavour and harmless specks of black mould. Tempeh is rich in **protein** and high in vitamins and minerals including **vitamin B$_{12}$**. It is easier to digest than most bean products due to the bacterial activity. It is normally sold frozen in small blocks.

PREPARATION: thaw the block and cut it into pieces or slices, which can then be stir-fried.

USES: most commonly used in Chinese and Japanese cuisine, especially stir-fries. Tempeh can also be added to casseroles and soups, or fried and eaten in **pitta bread**. Mashed tempeh can be used in casseroles and sauces as a substitute for minced meat.

253

temple orange   A red-skinned **citrus fruit**, which is sold as an **orange** but is in fact a cross between an orange and a **tangerine**.

tempura   A traditional Japanese dish and style of cooking, in which small pieces of a variety of foods are quickly deep-fried in a light, crisp batter. This style of cooking was traditionally applied to fish, but it is possible to cook **mushrooms** and other **vegetables** in this way.

textured vegetable protein (TVP)   A meat substitute manufactured commercially using **soya bean** flour. It is available as dehydrated chunks or 'mince', flavoured or unflavoured. It is commonly used as a meat extender in a variety of non-vegetarian manufactured foods, but although it aims to mimic closely the texture of meat it is essentially a vegetarian product.

Textured vegetable protein is a cheap and versatile product high in **protein** and **starch** and low in **fat**. It also contains useful amounts of **micronutrients** although some of these are unavailable due to its **phytic acid** content. Dry textured vegetable protein has a very long shelf life and should be stored in a sealed container.

PREPARATION: to hydrate textured vegetable protein, soak it in water or in vegetable **stock**.

USES: use hydrated textured vegetable protein mince or chunks exactly as you might use meat, for example in shepherd's pie or casseroles, or mixed with **herbs** and chopped, cooked vegetables and shaped into a 'meat' loaf or **burgers**.

Thai fragrant rice See **jasmine rice**.

thiamin (also called **vitamin B₁**) One of the **B complex vitamins**, essential for growth and metabolism, particularly concerned with the release of energy from **glucose**. Good vegetarian sources of vitamin B₁ include wholegrain **cereals**, **nuts**, **pulses**, **milk**, wholemeal **rice** and **pasta** and **yeast extract**. A diet that supplies adequate **carbohydrate** and **protein** will supply adequate amounts of thiamin.

thyme The leaves of a temperate shrub with a mint-like odour, which are used fresh or dried as a **herb**. Thyme should be stored in a sealed jar in a cool place to preserve its aroma.

USES: it goes well with **nut roasts** and stuffings, and in Italian-style **tomato** sauces.

tofu (also called **soya bean curd**) A smooth, bland, white curd made from the **soya bean**, sold in chilled, vacuum-packed blocks, or canned. Tofu originated in China. It is a highly nutritious and adaptable food which readily absorbs flavours and is often used as a **meat substitute**. It is high in good-quality **protein**, but very low in **fat**, and it also contains good amounts of **calcium** and

small amounts of **B complex vitamins**. There are
two main types of tofu: **firm** and **silken tofu**. The
texture depends upon how heavily the curd has
been pressed, and this will affect its use. Tofu is
also available flavoured, including **smoked** and
marinated tofu. It should be stored in the refrigerator and, once opened, kept covered with fresh
water, for not more than one week.

PREPARATION: firm tofu can be cut into large or
small chunks or slices, and added to casseroles or
stir-fries, or assembled as kebabs. Firm tofu takes
the flavour of marinades well. Silken tofu is softer
and better for mashing or puréeing with fruit for
desserts.

USES: use firm tofu in Chinese- and Japanese-
style meals as well as in savoury dishes, such as
curries, kebabs, stir-fries or fried with **soya sauce**.
Use silken tofu to make **vegan** cheesecakes,
creamy **yoghurt** desserts and **egg-free mayonnaise**.

tofulami A **meat substitute** commercially manufactured from **tofu** and flavoured and shaped to
resemble slices of salami sausage. It is sold
vacuum-packed and chilled and can be used as a
sandwich filling and pizza topping.

tomato The fleshy, red, many-seeded **fruit** of the
tomato plant, used as a vegetable. Fresh, canned,
dried and puréed tomatoes are widely used in vegetarian cookery, but they are not included in **macrobiotic diets** as they are a relative of the

nightshade family. Tomatoes come in a variety of sizes, from the sweet-tasting, bite-sized, cherry tomatoes to the rather watery, fist-sized beefsteak tomatoes. Tomatoes are high in water but offer some **carotene** and **vitamin C**. They can be stored in a plastic bag in the refrigerator for a week.

PREPARATION: tomatoes can be eaten raw (usually sliced or halved) or cooked. Halved tomatoes can be grilled or fried, and larger tomatoes may be stuffed and baked or served cold. A helpful tip if required to skin tomatoes is to drop them in boiling water for 15 seconds, the skins should then peel away easily.

USES: tomatoes are an essential ingredient of many casseroles, soups, sauces and savoury dishes, and are extensively used in Italian cuisine. Raw tomatoes can be used as a garnish or made into a salad, perhaps with slices of **mozzarella cheese**.

tomato purée A thick, red paste made from puréed and condensed **tomatoes**, commonly used to give flavour to casseroles and soups. It is sold in cans, jars and tubes.

tortiglione A variety of **pasta** shaped as spirals, which hold a **sauce** well, available in various colours. It is attractive used cold in salads.

trace elements **Minerals** necessary to the body in much smaller amounts than the major minerals.

These include: **copper**, **chromium**, **fluorine**, **iodine**, **iron**, **manganese**, **molybdenum**, **selenium** and **zinc**. In many cases their role in the body is not yet fully understood. Both deficiency and excessive intake can be avoided by maintaining a properly balanced diet containing a variety of foods. The vegetarian diet is not normally deficient in any trace elements. However, some foods, such as wholegrain **cereals** and **beans**, contain **phytic acid** which can hinder the absorption of certain trace elements and minerals.

treacle   See **black treacle**.

tree tomato   See **tamarillo**.

truffle   A rough-skinned, walnut-shaped fungus with solid, brownish-black flesh, which grows underground. It is native to France and Italy where it is found by trained dogs or pigs. In Britain truffles are mainly available canned. Fresh truffles should look plump with a dusty skin, and can be stored in the refrigerator covered with a layer of dry rice in a closed container.

PREPARATION: fresh truffles should be brushed to remove any surface dirt, rather than washed. Black (French) truffles are always cooked, and can be sautéed, added to sauces, casseroles or omelettes, or baked in puff pastry. White (Italian) truffles are not cooked but normally grated raw over cooked dishes.

USES: black truffles are used in casseroles and hot savoury dishes, and raw white truffles can be grated over cooked pasta or rice dishes. The rice used to store truffles will gain a new flavour and can be used to good effect in cooking.

turban squash A variety of **winter squash** shaped rather like a turban with a large, slightly flattened base topped with a rounded topknot. It can be prepared and used in the same way as **acorn squash**, and because of its unusual shape and wide range of colouration is also sometimes used hollowed out as an ornamental serving bowl.

turmeric The aromatic and yellow-coloured, underground stem of a tropical Asian plant, normally sold powdered and used as a **spice** to give flavour and colour to food. It should be stored in a dark glass jar in a cool place to preserve its taste and bright colour.

USES: mainly used to colour foods such as sauces, curries and rice.

turnip The root of a Mediterranean plant, with a green and white or purple skin and white or yellow flesh, eaten as a **vegetable**. Turnips have a high water content but contain some **sugars** and **dietary fibre** (including **pectins**). They do not contain significant quantities of any **micronutrients**. Small, firm turnips can be stored in a cool place for up to two weeks.

PREPARATION: small, early turnips can be washed and eaten raw, either sliced or grated into salads. Main crop turnips should be trimmed and peeled thickly. They can then be cut into pieces and boiled for around 30 minutes, or parboiled and roasted as you would **potatoes**.

USES: early turnips can be used in salads, but later turnips are best used in soups and casseroles or as a hot side vegetable. Once boiled, they can be mashed with **butter**, **salt** and **pepper** to taste. The flavour can be varied by mixing with mashed **carrot** or potato. Alternatively, serve pieces of cooked turnip in a **sauce**. See also **swede**.

TVP See **textured vegetable protein**.

tzatziki A Greek dip made from gated **cucumber** mixed with plain **yoghurt**, **garlic**, **olive oil** and **wine vinegar**. Tzatziki is widely available from delicatessens and may be kept stored in a refrigerator for several days.

USES: serve as a snack or starter with vegetable crudites or bread.

ugli fruit (also called **tangelo**) A large **citrus fruit** with loose, wrinkled, bumpy, greenish-yellow skin and tart, juicy, yellow flesh in crescent-shaped segments; it is the result of a cross between an **orange**, a **grapefruit** and a **tangerine**. Ugli fruits provide some **sugars**, **dietary fibre** and **vitamin C**.

PREPARATION: peel off the loose outer skin and then remove the skins from each segment.

USES: in fruit salads, or in marmalade.

ultra heat treated (UHT)   A method of sterilizing foods, usually **milk**, using very high temperatures. Ultra heat treatment is used to extend the shelf life of foods. It involves higher temperatures (130°C) than **pasteurization**, but over a shorter period (two seconds). Nutrient losses are similar to those that occur during pasteurization (25% loss of **vitamin C**, 10% loss of **thiamin**, **vitamin B₆**, **folic acid** and **vitamin B₁₂**), but UHT milk can be stored for long periods, though up to 50% loss of vitamin B₆ and vitamin B₁₂ will have occurred after three months of storage. Once the sealed container is opened, UHT milk is as perishable as pasteurized milk and should be kept in the refrigerator.

umeboshi plum   A variety of pink Japanese **plum** with an extremely sour taste, which is sold preserved in a jar of very salty water. In Japan they are thought to cleanse the system and are often eaten at breakfast. Umeboshi plums can be stoned and mashed or puréed to make a strong-tasting relish. The jar should be stored in the refrigerator.

unrefined oil   An **oil** extracted from **seeds**, **nuts** or **vegetables** without the use of chemicals, and filtered rather than treated with chemicals to remove any impurities. Unrefined oils are likely to retain more of the **micronutrients** found in their sorces than refined oils.

Valencia orange   A type of **orange** with thin, golden skin and sweet, juicy flesh without many seeds.

vanilla   The dark, aromatic pod of certain varieties of tropical climbing orchid, used for flavouring food. The pod may be ground up and used in food, or, more usually, soaked (e.g. in **milk**) to permeate the liquid with its flavour. Vanilla essence is made by extracting the oil that gives the pod its distinctive flavour. This essence and foods labelled 'vanilla flavour' may also contain artificial **flavouring** and **colourings**.

   USES: the pod can be used to infuse liquids or stored in a jar of caster **sugar** to flavour the sugar. Vanilla essence is used to flavour ice cream, cakes, biscuits, milk puddings and sweets.

vegan   A person who does not eat any food that comes from animals. This includes **milk** and **dairy products**, **eggs** and in many cases **honey**. Many vegans do not wear animal products, including leather, silk and wool. Strict vegans strive to avoid using any product which contains animal ingredients, including cosmetics and household cleaning products.

veganic gardening See **organic foods**.

vegetable The edible leaves, fruit, roots,
flowers or stalks of plants. Vegetables may be
eaten raw (in some cases) or cooked, and are available fresh, frozen, canned or dried. Vegetables
have low energy values because of their high water
contents. However, **root vegetables** contain more
starch and less water than non-root vegetables
and consequently have higher energy values. The
carbohydrate content of vegetables occurs as
sugars, starch and **dietary fibre** in varying
amounts. In general, vegetables provide little **protein** (although **pulses** are good plant sources of
protein) or **fat** (although vegetable **oils** and some
nuts are good sources). The amounts of **vitamins**
and **minerals** they contain varies, but most vegetables (especially dark green, leafy vegetables)
are important sources of **folic acid, riboflavin, vitamin A** (in the form of **carotene**) and **vitamin C**.
  Vitamin C and folic acid are easily destroyed by
poor cooking practices. In order to minimize
losses, vegetables should be cooked in a very small
amount of water for the shortest possible time.
Steaming or **microwaving** conserve the greatest
proportion of vitamins. See individual vegetable
entries.

vegetable concentrate A paste made from
puréed vegetables with the water content reduced.
It can be used to make **stock** and to flavour casseroles and soups.

vegetable fats Fats that are obtained from plant sources, rather than from animal sources.

vegetable juice Juice extracted from any of a variety of **vegetables**, such as **carrots**. The nutritional content of a vegetable juice depends upon what vegetable it is extracted from, but generally most include **vitamins A** and **C**. Vegetable juice can be purchased in bottles or cartons from health-food shops, and can be taken as a daily food supplement or served as an apéritif.

vegetable oils Oils derived from **seeds**, **nuts** or **vegetables**, all of which are suitable for vegetarians.

vegetable purée A purée of vegetables, often including **onion**, **celery** and **carrots**, sold in tubes. Vegetable purée can be used like **tomato purée** to flavour casseroles and soups and can be dissolved in water to make a **stock**.

vegetable suet Suet is a hard, white **fat** derived from animals and is not suitable for vegetarians, but a vegetarian suet is available which is made from solidified vegetable fat and is used in the same way as animal suet.

vegetarian A person who excludes from his or her diet any food or ingredient which is obtained by killing animals. This includes all meat, poultry, fish, shellfish and game, along with animal fats, **gelatine**, **suet** and **lard**. **Dairy products** and **eggs** are suitable for vegetarians, though many vegetarians prefer to avoid eating **battery eggs**. People who eat no red meat, but eat poultry and/or fish are sometimes called demi-vegetarians. See also the introductory sections.

veined cheese   Any of a variety of **cheeses** that have colourful (red, blue or green) veins of mould running through them. As yet only a few veined cheeses are made using **microbial rennet**.

vermicelli   A variety of **pasta** shaped like thin **spaghetti**, usually in coils. It cooks very quickly and can be used in clear soups and served with lightly **steamed** spring vegetables.

vinegar   A sharp-tasting, acidic liquid, consisting of impure dilute acetic acid (which gives it its sour taste), which is produced by bacterial activity in fermented liquids, such as beer, cider or wine. The word is derived from the French *vin aigre*, 'sour wine'. Vinegar is used for flavouring foods and as a preservative in pickled foods. Malt vinegar is used mainly as a preservative and more delicately flavoured vinegars, such as **wine vinegar**, **cider vinegar** and **herb vinegars**, are used to add flavour and make salad dressings. The food colouring caramel is often used to colour vinegar brown. See also **balsamic vinegar**; **raspberry vinegar**.

vine leaves (also called **grape leaves**)   The large, five-pointed, flat leaves of the **grape** vine. They are native to Greece and the Middle East, but are usually sold in most countries vacuum-packed in plastic bags of brine.

PREPARATION: the leaves should be rinsed several times and if they are to be stuffed they should be **blanched** by soaking them in boiling water for 15 minutes.

USES: the main use for vine leaves is to make dolmas or dolmades, a Middle-Eastern dish consisting of parcels of cooked **rice** with **onions**, **garlic**, **herbs** and **olive oil** wrapped in a vine leaf and sometimes served with a **tomato** sauce. Fresh vine leaves can be used as a garnish for **cheese** and grape platters.

virgin olive oil   See **extra virgin olive oil**.

vitamin A (also called **retinol**)   A **vitamin** essential for growth and for the maintenance of healthy skin and mucous membranes in the eyes, ears, nose, throat, lungs and bladder. Retinol is only found in animal foods and vegetarians obtain it in **dairy products** and **eggs**. Carotene is the precursor of vitamin A and vegetarians and vegans can manufacture their own retinol by ensuring a good intake of carotene, which is found in many orange-coloured and green leafy vegetables.

vitamin B₁   See **thiamin**.

vitamin B₂   See riboflavin.

vitamin B₃   See niacin.

vitamins B₄, B₇, B₉, B₁₀, B₁₄, B₁₆   These are vitamins no longer considered essential to humans.

vitamin B₅   See pantothenic acid.

vitamin B₆ (also called pyridoxine)   One of the B complex vitamins, which is essential for growth and is a key factor in the formation of haemoglobin for red blood cells. It has also been linked with the conversion of linoleic acid into other essential fatty acids, the maintenance of a correct sodium and potassium balance, and the formation of antibodies and red blood cells. Vegetarian sources include cheese, eggs, wholegrain cereals and wholemeal bread, many vegetables, nuts, bananas, avocados and brewer's yeast.

vitamin B₁₂ (also called cyanocobalamin)   One of the B complex vitamins vital for growth and for the correct formation of red blood cells. It is also important to the maintenance of a healthy nervous system because it helps form the fatty sheath around nerves. Vitamin B₁₂ is only available in animal foods, including dairy products and eggs, although research continues in an attempt to discover a vegan source. Vegans are advised to

267

include fortified foods such as **yeast extract** or **soya milk** in their diets or to take a vitamin B$_{12}$ supplement.

vitamin C (also called **ascorbic acid**) A **vitamin** essential for growth and vital for the formation of collagen, a protein necessary to healthy bones, teeth, skin, gums, blood capillaries and all connective tissues. Vitamin C is important for the healing of wounds and fractures, and increases the absorption of **iron**, while helping to excrete toxic minerals such as lead, copper and mercury. The best sources are **blackcurrants**, **broccoli**, **green peppers**, **strawberries**, **cabbage**, fresh **citrus fruits**, **potatoes**, **peas**, **parsley**, **spinach** and **watercress**. A diet high in fresh fruit and vegetables, raw where possible, will provide ample vitamin C.

vitamin D A **vitamin** essential for growth, for the absorption of **calcium** from food and for the hardening of bones with calcium and **phosphorus**. It also assists in maintaining a healthy nervous system and sound circulation. Vitamin D can be synthesized and stored by the body when the skin is exposed to sunlight. It occurs naturally in **milk**, **dairy products** and **eggs**. Vegetarians and vegans who are confined indoors, or who have religious beliefs which involve covering up much of the skin, may wish to include fortified foods such as **soya milk** in their diets, or to take a vitamin D supplement. Vitamin D$_2$ is always from a plant source.

vitamin E (also called **tocopherol**) An **antioxidant**, vital for maintaining the structure of cell membranes. Good sources of vitamin E are **asparagus**, **avocados**, polyunsaturated **margerine**, **nuts** and **vegetable oils**. Vitamin E deficiency is very rare because of its wide distribution in foods and because of the small requirement.

vitamin H See **biotin**.

vitamin K A **vitamin** essential to the production of several **proteins**, including prothrombin which is involved in blood clotting. It has been found to exist in three forms, one of which (vitamin K_1) is obtained from food and the other two are synthesized within the body. Vitamin K_1 is present in all green, leafy vegetables, **broccoli**, **cereals**, **spinach**, **alfalfa**, **safflower seed oil**, **soya oil** and **seaweeds**, and is unaffected by cooking and processing. Vitamin K deficiency is rare because vitamins K_2 and K_3 can be synthesized in the body.

vitamins Any of a number of organic substances needed by the body in very small amounts to help growth, metabolism and general health. Vitamins cannot be synthesized by the body and must be supplied by the diet. A balanced vegetarian diet can supply every essential vitamin. However, **vitamin B_{12}** is not available in plant foods, and neither is **vitamin D**, although the latter can be produced by the body when in the presence of sunlight. **Vegans** may wish to consider supplementing their diet with vitamin pills or special fortified foods.

wakame A variety of **seaweed** native to Japan, which is related to **kombu** and can be mistaken for kombu when it is dried, though when it is rehydrated it regains its green colour. Wakame is rich in **calcium**, **B complex vitamins** and **vitamin C**. It has a mild taste and is a good introduction to cooking and eating sea vegetables.

PREPARATION: soak for five minutes in cold water until the dried leaves unfurl. The thick midrib of the leaves can be torn out if preferred. Wakame may be served cold or simmered for 10 minutes. It can also be added dry to simmering soups or crumbled onto cooked foods.

USES: as a salad or hot side vegetable, or in soups, especially Japanese miso soup. Crumbled dried wakame can be sprinkled onto **rice** and other **grain** dishes as a nutritious condiment.

walnut The **nut** of a deciduous tree with a hard, wrinkled shell and an oily, two-lobed kernel. Walnuts have a high-**fat** content with a high proportion of **polyunsaturated fats**. Walnuts contain **potassium** (but not as much as other nuts), **dietary fibre**, **starch** and **sugars**. They are rich in **phosphorus** and contain some **thiamin**, **vitamin B$_6$**, **folic acid** and **biotin**. They are normally sold shelled and will keep for a long time in a sealed container.

PREPARATION: walnuts can be eaten as they are, or chopped or ground.

USES: in fruit cakes and chopped with **muesli**. Walnuts can be added to salads and incorporated into **burgers** and bakes.

walnut oil A dark, fragrant vegetable **oil** extracted from **walnuts**, which is used for its flavour in salad dressings. It is high in **polyunsaturated fats**.

water chestnut (also called **Chinese water chestnut**) The succulent corm (a root, not in fact a **nut**) of a Chinese, water-dwelling plant with crunchy, white, sweet-tasting flesh. Water chestnuts are widely available canned, but have more flavour when fresh. Fresh water chestnuts may be available from specialist Chinese food shops.

PREPARATION: peel away the flaky brown skin and use whole or chopped.

USES: mainly in traditional Chinese cuisine, such as stir-fries and sweet-and-sour dishes.

watercress A leafy, green vegetable grown in running fresh water. Although it has a high water content and little **protein** or **dietary fibre**, it is rich in **vitamin A, folic acid, riboflavin** and **vitamin C**, as well as **potassium** and **calcium**. It does not keep well but can be stored in a plastic bag in the refrigerator for one or two days.

PREPARATION: trim the bases of the stalks and any discoloured leaves and rinse well in cold water. Watercress is generally used raw but it can be sautéed in butter.

USES: as a salad leaf vegetable, or as a garnish or sandwich filling. It can also be used to make hot or chilled watercress soup, or as a hot side vegetable.

watermelon A variety of **melon** that is often very large, with dark green, smooth skin and juicy but insipid pink flesh with many inedible black seeds.

Welsh onion (also called **Japanese bunching onion**) A perennial plant not unlike **chives**, which has thin, tubular leaves up to two feet tall and an **onion** flavour. It is not normally commercially available.

PREPARATION: trim the leaves and rinse thoroughly in cold water.

USES: as a substitute for chives or **spring onions** in salads, **quiches**, omelettes and a wide variety of dishes.

wheat A **cereal** that is a major source of **carbohydrate** and **protein** in the western diet. Wheat **flour** is the main ingredient of **bread**, and wheat is also used to make breakfast cereals and **pasta**. Whole-wheat grains (called 'berries') are available from health-food shops. To make white flour, wheat grains are milled to remove the germ and bran, and this seriously depletes their nutritional value.

PREPARATION: whole-wheat grains can be cooked like **rice**. They need to be simmered in boiling water for two hours or more. **Cracked wheat** (whole wheat grains subjected to hydraulic pressure to crack them) and kibbled wheat (broken whole grains) cook more quickly.

USES: whole, cracked or kibbled wheat can be used in salads, **burgers** or bakes. Wheat flakes can be used as a breakfast food or as part of a savoury crumble mixture. People who are vegetarian for health reasons often aim for a 'wholefood' diet and prefer to use unrefined brown flour for all their cooking requirements.

wheat bran   See **bran**.

wheat germ   The embryo in the wheat seed, situated at the bottom of the **grain**. The wheat germ contains much of the nutritional value of the grain and is rich in **protein** and **fat**, with a high proportion of unsaturated fats. It is one of the best sources of **vitamin E** and the **B complex vitamins**, and is also a good source of **iron**, **phosphorus** and a number of other **micronutrients**. Because of its high fat content it may go rancid unless stored in the refrigerator. There is a processed wheat germ available which has been treated to prevent rancidity and virtually all the nutrients are retained.

USES: wheat germ is used as a nutritional supplement and can be sprinkled onto cooked foods and yoghurt or mixed with flour for baking.

whey   A watery liquid, created as a by-product of the cheesemaking industry, where it is separated from milk using **rennet**. Curds (see **curd cheese**) are the other product of this process. Whey is commonly used as a food additive and features in a wide range of manufactured foods, including confectionery. Because the production of whey almost always involves the use of animal rennet, strict vegetarians do not include whey in their diets.

white cabbage   See **white salad cabbage**.

white currant   The small, round, white berries of a temperate shrub similar to a **redcurrant**. They are less acidic than redcurrants, with a flavour similar to grapes. White currants are not widely commercially available, though they may be bought from some farms where you are able to pick your own fruit.

PREPARATION: strip the berries from the clusters with a fork. The tiny stems can be left on the berries as removing them is a time-consuming and sticky task. They can then be rinsed in cold water and served fresh or stewed.

USES: as a contrast to redcurrants or **blackcurrants** in tarts, on cheesecakes, in pies and in fresh fruit salads.

white pepper   A hot-tasting powder made by grinding **peppercorns**, which have been allowed to dry on the plant and have then been treated to remove the outer husks. It is available as a powder, or as whole peppercorns that may be ground as required in a peppermill. White pepper is used in the same way as **black pepper**, and white peppercorns can be mixed with black peppercorns in a clear plastic or glass peppermill for a decorative effect.

USES: as a **spice** to give a hot taste to a variety of foods.

white radish   See **daikon**.

white rice   Any of a variety of types of **rice** that has been milled to remove the husk and outer layer of **bran**. White rice lacks the **dietary fibre**, **B complex vitamins** and other **micronutrients** available in wholegrain brown rice. However, it is more popular than brown rice.

PREPARATION: cook 250 g of white **long-grain rice** in 500 ml of water for 15 minutes, or in a medium oven for 40 minutes. White **basmati rice** cooks more quickly (10 minutes, or 35 minutes in the oven) in less water (450 ml).

USES: as an accompaniment to casseroles, curries, chilli, stir-fries, or use to stuff vegetables or cold in a salad. See also **risotto rice**.

white salad cabbage   A variety of **cabbage** popular as a salad vegetable. Like other varieties of cabbage, it is a good source of **potassium**, **vitamin C** and **folic acid**. White salad cabbages should be very firm and crisp and can be stored, wrapped in clingfilm, in the refrigerator for up to one week.

PREPARATION: white cabbage may be eaten raw, shredded into salads or stir-fried. The leaves can be **blanched** and then stuffed and baked or boiled as you would **vine leaves**.

USES: commonly raw in coleslaw salads or as a hot side vegetable. Boiled cabbage is best served in a sauce, or sprinkled with **cheese** and grilled.

white wine vinegar   A variety of **wine vinegar** made with white **wine**.

wholefood diet   A diet frequently adopted by vegetarians for health reasons, which involves eating as many foods as possible in their raw and unrefined state. Wholefoods include, for example, brown **rice** and other unrefined **cereals**, **nuts**, **seeds**, **pulses**, fresh **fruit** and fresh **vegetables** (raw where possible). Unrefined wholefoods are likely to contain more **vitamins** as well as a wider range of **trace elements** than processed foods. They are also lower in **salt** and **sugar**, and higher in **dietary fibre** than processed foods. See INTRODUCTION, VEGETARIAN NUTRITION.

wholegrain (also called **wholemeal**)   Grains of **cereals** that have not been refined in processing to remove any part of the grain. Most of the **B com-**

plex vitamins, fat, dietary fibre, iron, trace elements and **vitamin E** are concentrated in the **bran**, germ and outer layers of the endosperm. The nutritional content of the cereal is reduced the more it is refined. Many vegetarians prefer to follow a **wholefood diet** were possible, that is, including within the diet unrefined cereals and unprocessed **fruit** and **vegetables**. Wholemeal brown **flour**, **bread** and **pasta** are made using unmilled wholegrains. See also **wheat germ**.

whortleberry See **blueberry**.

wild foods A variety of **fruits**, **fungi**, leaves and **seaweeds** that are not commercially available, but can be harvested seasonally from the wild. Due care must be given to identifying edible items correctly and to harvesting from untainted areas, to avoid food poisoning due to false identification or to eating unripe or tainted foods. Some vegetarians especially enjoy the chance to eat food directly supplied by nature. It is wise to invest in an illustrated book if you wish to do this. See **dandelion**; **nettle**; **rowanberry**; **sloe**.

wild rice A variety of **cereal** with black grains that resemble **long-grain rice**, although it is not a member of the **rice** family. Wild rice is native to the Great Lakes of North America, and because it is difficult to harvest it is more expensive than other grains. It is often sold mixed with brown rice.

PREPARATION: cook in the same way as brown long-grain rice; 250 g require 750 ml of water and should be allowed to simmer for 45 minutes. A mixture of brown and wild rice should be cooked until the brown is tender, while the wild rice retains a distinctive 'bite'.

USES: due to its expense it is rarely used as a single grain. It adds variety to a savoury rice dish, and is excellent in stuffed vegetables.

wine An alcoholic drink usually made by fermenting **grapes**, although it may be made by fermenting many kinds of fruit or flower in this way. In grape wine, the grapes used may be black (red wine) or white (white wine) or both may be used (rosé wine). Varying amounts of sugar and water are added during the fermenting process to produce sweet, medium or dry wines.

Certain wines are considered unsuitable for strict vegetarians because their manufacture involves the use of **gelatine**, **isinglass**, **battery eggs** or other products unsuitable for vegetarians. Although in practice these ingredients are often used as clearing agents, which come to rest at the bottom of the fermenting vessel and do not appear in the bottle or glass. Current labelling laws do not require these ingredients to be listed, though a few wines carry the Vegetarian Society's 'V' symbol. Many vegetarians prefer to drink organic wine where possible. This is made from organically grown grapes and is free from agricultural chemicals, and also from chemicals sometimes added during the manufacturing process to non-organic wines (see also **organic foods**). Importers of organic wines are often knowledgeable about individual production methods and may list vegetarian and vegan wines in their mail-order catalogues. There are some vegetarians who do not drink alcohol for health or moral reasons.

wine vinegar   Vinegar that has been made from wine; either red or white wine may be used. It has a lighter taste than malt vinegar and is used in salad dressings and marinades. See also **balsamic vinegar**; **cider vinegar**; **herb vinegar**; **raspberry vinegar**.

winged pea   See **asparagus pea**.

winter melon   The name given to **melons**, including the **honeydew** and **lavan melons**, that have a large, oval shape and very thick, hard-ribbed, skin which may be either yellow or green. The flesh is crisp and juicy but has a tendency to be insipid and even when ripe does not smell fragrant.

winter squash   The name given to **squashes**, including **acorn squash**, **butternut squash**, **spaghetti squash** and **pumpkins**, which have firm flesh and tough, hard skins. They are harvested in the summer and autumn but are called 'winter'

279

because they can be stored for many months. Winter squashes are always cooked before eating and have a sweet, nutty-tasting flesh.

Worcester or **Worcestershire sauce** A thin, brown, spicy sauce which traditionally includes anchovies amongst its ingredients. In general, Worcester sauce is not suitable for vegetarians, and they should be aware that it is sometimes used as a **flavouring** in manufactured foods. A brand of Worcester sauce that does not contain anchovies is available from health-food shops.

yam The starchy tuber of any of various tropical, twining plants. Although it is sometimes called **sweet potato**, it is actually a quite different vegetable, having oily, orange- rather than floury, yellow-flesh. Yams are also much larger than sweet potatoes. They are high in **starch**, provide a little **protein** and **dietary fibre** (including **pectin**), and a small amount of **sugars**. They have a higher **Calorie** value than potatoes and are lower in **vitamins B** and **C**.

PREPARATION: peel and cut into pieces for boiling or frying. Yams may also be roasted, but they do not bake successfully.

USES: as a hot side vegetable. Yams can also be used in curries and fruity, West Indian-style casseroles.

yam flour   A starchy, **gluten**-free **flour** derived
from **yams**. It is available from some health-food
shops or by mail-order from specialist outlets.
  USES: in baking, alone or mixed with other
flours.

yard-long bean   See **asparagus bean**.

yeast   A substance consisting of single-celled
fungi of the genus *Saccharomyces*, available as
dried granules or as a cheesy culture with a distinctive yeasty aroma. In baking, yeast is used to
make dough rise. This is because in the presence of
sugars and in a warm, moist atmosphere it repro-
duces rapidly and releases carbon dioxide, which
causes the dough to expand. Yeast is also used in
brewing certain beers, because it ferments the
sugars in the cereals used. **Brewer's yeast** is a rich
source of some **vitamins** and **minerals**, especially
the **B complex vitamins**. Yeast is suitable for both
vegetarians and vegans. See also **yeast extract**.

yeast extract   A savoury paste made by autoly-
sis (self-digestion) of the cell walls of the **yeast** so
that the contents are released. Yeast extract is
important in the vegetarian and vegan diet, partly
for its ability to flavour foods and partly because it
is a rich source of **B complex vitamins**, including
vitamin B$_{12}$. It also provides **iron**, **calcium** and
phosphorus. Generally, because **salt** is added,
yeast extract is high in **sodium**, though salt-free
brands are available from health-food shops.

USES: yeast extract can be dissolved in water to make a stock or a savoury hot drink, and can be added by the teaspoon to simmering casseroles, soups and sauces. It can be used as a nutritious and low-**Calorie** spread on bread or rice cakes, and is sometimes included in the diet specifically as a nutritional supplement.

yellow split pea   See **split pea**.

yellow squash   A variety of **summer squash** with easily blemished, yellow skin. It is at its best when less than seven inches long. Yellow squashes have a high water content and a similar nutritional profile to **courgettes**. They can be stored, wrapped in paper, in the refrigerator for one or two days.

PREPARATION: prepare as courgettes. Wash and slice or cut into pieces and then lightly steam or sauté with herbs. Yellow squash can be grated raw into salads and can also be halved and stuffed like a small marrow.

USES: yellow squash can be used as a hot side vegetable, but is more successful sautéed with other vegetables, **olive oil** and **spices**, or stuffed with a savoury nut or grain mixture, or added to rich soups and casseroles.

yoghurt   A thick, custard-like dairy product made by curdling **milk** with certain strains of bacteria. Yoghurt can be made from whole, **semi-skimmed** or **skimmed milk**, or from **goats'** or **ewes'**

milk, and there are **vegan** brands available which are made with **soya milk**. It is cheap and easy to make at home.

Yoghurt is a nutritious and easily-digested food, which is high in **protein** and **calcium**, and also contains **iron** and the **B complex vitamins**. Its **fat** contant depends upon the type of milk from which it is made. Commercially-prepared yoghurts may be very high in **sugar** and may contain artificial **colourings** and **gelatine** as a thickening agent.

Some yoghurts, called live or bio-yoghurts, contain living bacteria, which are said to be of benefit to the digestive system, although this has not yet been proved.

PREPARATION: to make yoghurt at home you must first purchase a carton of live, unflavoured yoghurt. Bring a pint of milk (550 ml) to the boil, then leave it to cool until it reaches blood temperature. Stir in one dessertspoonful of the live yoghurt and mix it in well. Put the warm mixture in a thermos flask, in a bowl in the airing cupboard or in a special yoghurt-making machine where there will be constant gentle warmth. The live bacteria should convert the mixture to yoghurt within eight hours. It should then be refrigerated until needed, and a spoonful reserved for starting the next batch.

USES: as a healthy snack, with fruit, nuts or muesli, or as a lower-**Calorie** alternative to cream with fruit salad. It can also be flavoured with honey and spices such as cinnamon. It can be used to make a salad dressing or dip, or swirled decoratively onto a bowl of soup.

zeitan See seitan.

zinc A **trace element** that is an essential component of many **enzyme** systems. It is vital for growth and sexual maturation and it has a function in wound healing. Zinc is found in greatest amount in meat, **dairy products** and **eggs**. Nuts, **wholegrains**, **vegetables** and **pulses** also contain zinc, but it is not so well digested as the zinc in animal foods.

zucchini See courgette.

COLLINS GEM

Other Gem titles that may interest you include:

Gem Healthy Eating and Nutrition
A compact guide to the nutritional values of
everyday foodstuffs and drinks   **£2.99**

Gem Food Additives
An invaluable directory of over 1300 terms relating
to food additives   **£2.99**

Gem Food for Freezing
Describes food suitable for freezing, food
preparation techniques, and freezing and
thawing methods   **£2.99**

Gem Food for Microwaving
Contains everything you need to know about
microwaving food at home   **£2.99**

Gem Calorie Counter
New revised edition, with additional nutritional
information for thousands of branded foods   **£2.99**

Gem Herbs for Cooking and Health
Details how to grow and use the range of herbs that
have traditionally been used in cooking and
medicine   **£3.50**

COLLINS GEM

Bestselling Collins Gem titles include:

Gem English Dictionary (£3.50)
Gem Calorie Counter (£2.99)
Gem Thesaurus (£2.99)
Gem French Dictionary (£3.50)
Gem German Dictionary (£3.50)
Gem Basic Facts Mathematics (£2.99)
Gem Birds (£3.50)
Gem Babies' Names (£3.50)
Gem Card Games (£3.50)
Gem Atlas of the World (£3.50)

All Collins Gems are available from your local bookseller or can be ordered direct from the publishers.

In the UK, contact Mail Order, Dept 2M, HarperCollins Publishers, Westerhill Rd, Bishopbriggs, Glasgow, G64 2QT, listing the titles required and enclosing a cheque or p.o. for the value of the books plus £1.00 for the first title and 25p for each additional title to cover p&p. Access and Visa cardholders can order on 041-772 2281 (24 hr).

In Australia, contact Customer Services, HarperCollins Distribution, Yarrawa Rd, Moss Vale 2577 (tel. [048] 68 0300). In New Zealand, contact Customer Services, HarperCollins Publishers, 31 View Rd, Glenfield, Auckland 10 (tel. [09] 444 3740). In Canada, contact your local bookshop.

All prices quoted are correct at time of going to press.